The Bridge Knows The Way

Watson Mill/Carlton Bridge, Georgia, 1991

THE BRIDGE KNOWS THE WAY

Seeing America Through Covered Bridges

by
Frank F. Tobie

MILLWOOD PUBLISHING
Spokane, Washington
2004

Library of Congress Cataloging-in-Publication Data

Tobie, Frank F.
  The bridge knows the way : seeing America through covered bridges /
by Frank F. Tobie.
     p. cm.
  Includes bibliographical references and index.
  ISBN 0-87062-333-8 (hardcover : alk. paper)
  1. Covered bridges--United States. 2. Covered bridges--Canada. I.
Title.
  TG23.T63 2004
  624.2'18'097--dc22
                              2004005292

To my wife
Elizabeth
companion in visiting the more than
one hundred covered bridges included in this book
assisting in photographing bridges
and helping to describe the experience.

To our daughters, Mary and Susan, and son, Milton,
for pitching in to help finish the task.

CONTENTS

Diagrams and Maps

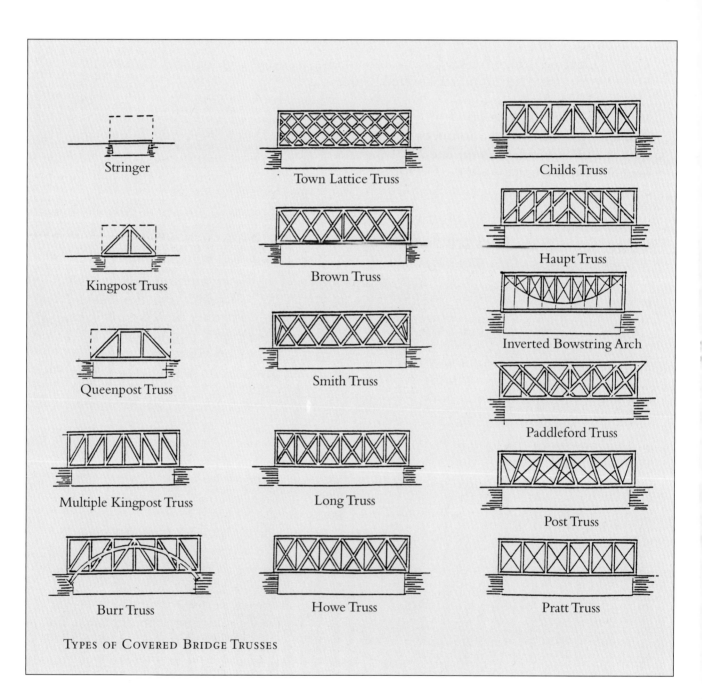

Stringer

Kingpost Truss

Queenpost Truss

Multiple Kingpost Truss

Burr Truss

Town Lattice Truss

Brown Truss

Smith Truss

Long Truss

Howe Truss

Childs Truss

Haupt Truss

Inverted Bowstring Arch

Paddleford Truss

Post Truss

Pratt Truss

TYPES OF COVERED BRIDGE TRUSSES

Chapter One

INTRODUCTION TO COVERED BRIDGES

Covered Bridge Fever

Covered bridges have existed in North America for two hundred years. Today, more than one thousand remain in twenty-nine of the United States and four Canadian provinces. Interesting, varied in design and appearance, and remarkably durable, the bridges are a significant part of our American heritage.

My wife Elizabeth and I discovered a covered bridge near our hometown of Spokane, Washington, in 1969, and our love affair with these fascinating structures began. In 1982, we visited covered bridges as part of our vacation in Oregon. In 1986, we continued our search for these unique bridges in the Québec and New Brunswick provinces of Canada, and in Maine, New Hampshire, and Vermont in New England. With the help of our daughters, Mary and Susan, and our son Milton, we managed to accomplish our goal of visiting and photographing at least one covered bridge in each of the states or provinces where covered bridges can still be found.

In this narrative, we will be your guides as we visit one hundred covered bridges. Our trip will begin in Spokane, Washington, and it will seem that we travel from bridge to bridge all in one trip, but to be fair, we will provide clues to when we actually visited each bridge. We will present to you real bridges as we saw and learned about them. This tour is all about travel, fun, and entertainment. We hope you will enjoy, as much as we did, learning about these magnificent structures.

Why the truss? And why cover the truss?

THE TRUSS

Early bridges built across rivers and streams were usually made of wood, the most practical material available at that time. The simplest wood bridge was constructed with wood beams reaching from bank to bank and a wood deck laid on top of the beams. This basic bridge, known as a "stringer," would sag under heavy loads, but was adequate for short spans.

The truss combined individual wood beams into a structure capable of supporting considerable weight, much more weight than a stringer (see page 65). Trusses were usually constructed in pairs, one on each side of the bridge, with the bridge deck in between. The truss could be as simple as the "Kingpost" (a triangle with a vertical post in the middle), the "Queenpost" (which I refer to as a "stretch Kingpost," see page 63), the "Multiple Kingpost" (repeating the Kingpost, see page 53), and a variety of patented trusses bearing the names of their inventors. More than two-thirds of the one hundred covered bridges on our tour in this book have a Burr Truss (page 42), a Town Lattice Truss (page 90), or a Howe Truss (page 19) for their support. Other trusses include the Long, Brown, Childs (page 49), Haupt, Paddleford, Post, Pratt, and Smith trusses, and the Inverted Bowstring Arch (page 49). (Page numbers indicate photographic examples of these trusses.) All of the structural types are included in the drawings on the facing page.

Theodore Burr found that the strength of the Multiple Kingpost Truss could be substantially increased by adding an arch. His Waterford Bridge built in 1804 across the Hudson River stood for 105 years. He patented the Burr Truss in 1805.

Ithiel Town was an architect. His design (the Town Lattice Truss) consisted of diagonal crossing beams, creating a lattice effect, with the beams joined together by wooden pegs. The truss was readily adaptible to any reasonable length. The Town Lattice Truss was patented in 1820.

The Long Truss was designed by Bvt. Lt. Colonel Stephen H. Long, U.S. Army Topographical Engineers. His truss with crossed diagonal and vertical wood beams was patented in 1830.

William Howe made a significant change to the design of Stephen Long by substituting vertical iron rods for the vertical wood beams. The iron rods, threaded and with bolts on the ends, could be tightened regularly to maintain the strength and rigidity of the truss. He patented the Howe Truss in 1840.

WHY COVER THE TRUSS?

Why were the bridges covered? When exposed to rain, the wooden trusses on each side of the bridge deck begin to rot at the joints. Uncovered, the trusses deteriorate rapidly, lasting perhaps twenty years. Covered and maintained, they last many more years. The siding and roof help keep the structural wood beams dry and strong. The cost of a roof and siding was much less than the cost of replacing the truss or the entire bridge.

Many covered bridges have stood for one hundred years. In the United States today, covered bridges built as early as 1820 are still standing. The Hyde Hall Bridge in New York and the Pulp Mill Bridge in Vermont have been standing for about 180 years.

The Bridge Numbering System

Basic information about each covered bridge, such as the name, year it was built, its length, the number of spans, the type of truss, and the bridge number, is available in the World Guide to Covered Bridges published by the National Society for the Preservation of Covered Bridges. The bridge numbering system, established by the National Society, ensures that each bridge has a unique identification.

Thus, White Bridge (22-34-01) in Michigan can be distinguished from another White Bridge (38-30-30) in Pennsylvania. The first two numbers identify the state alphabetically starting with the state, Alabama (01), or province, British Columbia (51). The next two, or occasionally three, numbers identify alphabetically the county within the state or province, and the last two numbers are a unique number within the county for that covered bridge. Thus, for White Bridge, the number (22-34-01) represents Michigan (22), Ionia County (34), and the first numbered covered bridge within the county (01).

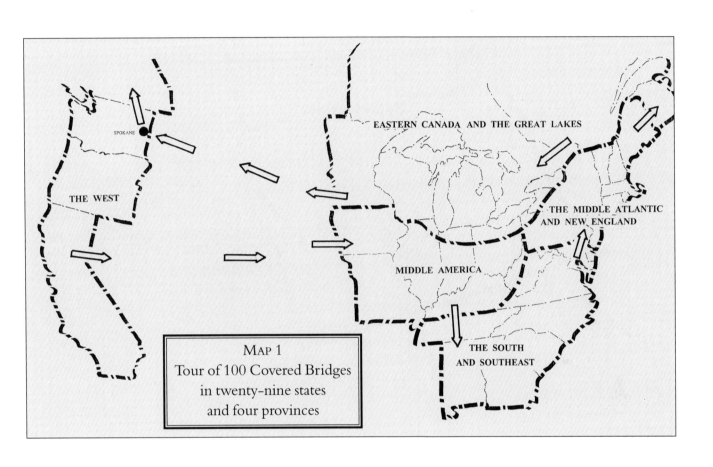

THE WEST

SPOKANE

EASTERN CANADA AND THE GREAT LAKES

THE MIDDLE ATLANTIC
AND NEW ENGLAND

MIDDLE AMERICA

THE SOUTH
AND SOUTHEAST

MAP 1
Tour of 100 Covered Bridges
in twenty-nine states
and four provinces

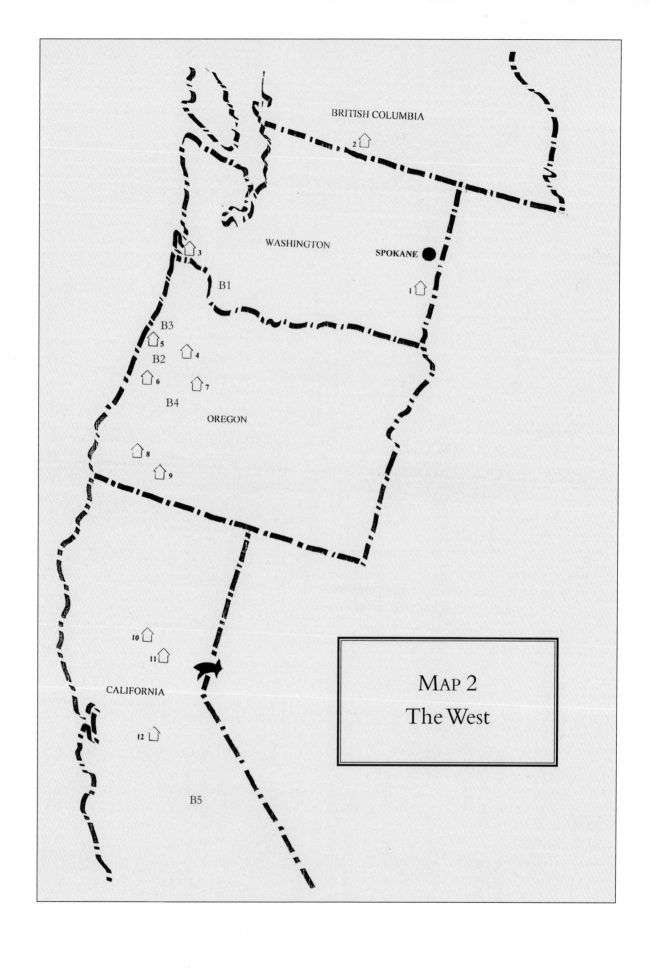

BRITISH COLUMBIA

2

WASHINGTON

SPOKANE

3

1

B1

B3

5

4

B2

6

7

B4

OREGON

8

9

10

11

CALIFORNIA

12

B5

MAP 2
The West

Chapter Two

The West

1 *Close to Home*

Colfax/Road Bridge (47-38-01) built in 1922 with one 163-foot Howe Truss span across the Palouse River near Colfax, Washington.

Spokane, Washington, has been home for my wife Elizabeth and I since 1951, seven years after we met, and we have lived there most of the time since. But travel is in our blood, and we love vacations and weekend drives. Winter is slow arriving, the roads are clear, and we are off on a Saturday drive in December, 1969 south from Spokane toward Colfax on a primitive road.

The road makes a sharp turn and suddenly crosses the tracks of the Great Northern Railroad. Occasional freight trains still use the tracks and no special warning devices are in place at the railroad crossings. Ahead, across a misty field, a grain elevator sits beside the railroad tracks. A few miles beyond, at Manning, is another grain elevator. The tracks lead from it to a covered railroad bridge straddling the Palouse River. From the road, we have a view of the bridge, the river, and the surrounding woods. It is a charming scene, so we stop to take a photograph.

This is the Colfax/Road Bridge, built in 1922. Before the Great Northern Railroad purchased it, the line was an electrified interurban line carrying passengers and freight between Spokane, Colfax, and other Palouse points. After Great Northern ended operations in the area, the owners of the land south of the river converted the bridge to a road bridge providing private access to their farm. This unconventional wooden bridge is open at the top to allow for the over-

head trolley line. It is called a covered bridge, even without a roof, because the trusses supporting it are covered.

We had, by taking that back road in 1969, chanced on a covered bridge we otherwise would have missed. The scene haunted us, and we returned in 1970, again in 1988 with a zoom lens to get a close-up of the bridge, and in 1997 to make sure it was still there. It was.

We invite you to take this trip with us as we relive our earlier visits to one hundred covered bridges in the United States and Canada.

Our tour begins at Colfax, and we go north on U.S. Highway 195, left on Washington State Highway 26, immediately turn right on Green Hollow Road, go four and one-half miles, and turn left on Manning Road for three-quarters of a mile to Manning.

We return to U.S. 195 north of Colfax, then go north to Spokane, north and west to the Grand Coulee Dam and on to British Columbia.

The Grand Coulee Dam on the Columbia River has been a favorite destination for our family since we moved to Spokane. The immensity of the structure is difficult to grasp in the majestic setting with the Columbia River and the Grand Coulee topography as a backdrop. When we go inside one of the two powerhouses, view the long row of giant turbines, and feel the vibration as much of the river passes through the turbines, the immensity of the dam becomes apparent.

Today, with a third powerhouse added, most of the water goes through the turbines and very lit-

15

1. Colfax/Road Bridge, Washington, 1969

One Way to Cross a Bridge

Ashnola River Road Bridge (52-06-02) west of Keremeos, British Columbia. Built in 1923 with three Howe Truss spans and a 400-foot crossing of Similkameen River.

tle over the dam. The Bureau of Reclamation maintains a visitor center and presents programs that explain much of the history and function of Grand Coulee Dam. In the summer, a laser light show at night is entertaining and educational, and water is allowed to flow over the dam at the end of the show. A portion of the electricity generated is used to pump water up to the Big Bend area where it is used for irrigation. Water has transformed a once marginal, arid area into rich farmland. Above the dam, at Spring Canyon, we pause to picnic and swim. It is a convenient stopping point for an appetizing breakfast cooked over an open fire or for a picnic lunch from home.

Next, we continue to Keremeos (pronounced "Kah-RAY-mee-us"), British Columbia. Many alternate routes are available as we travel between covered bridges. We'll describe some of our favorites, but you may choose your own.

In the 1920s, the Great Northern Railroad built a spur line north from Pateros, Washington, into British Columbia. The line followed the Similkameen River with covered bridge crossings near Oroville, Nighthawk, International Boundary (six miles north of the border), and Keremeos. The Ashnola River Road Bridge is just west of Keremeos and is a former railroad bridge with three pairs of huge trusses. Like the Colfax/Road Bridge, it is also roofless. Great Northern built bridges this way to allow sparks and smoke from the steam engines to escape, reducing the danger of setting the bridges ablaze. The Ashnola River Road Bridge has been con-

16

Grand Coulee Dam,
Washington, 1956

2. Ashnola River Road Bridge, British Columbia, 1989

verted to a road bridge, with the rails replaced by wood planking. The bridge provides access to Cathedral Provincial Park, a recreational area extending south along the Ashnola River to the United States border.

The bridge and the approach viaduct are wide enough for one car, so take a long look ahead. If no one is approaching from the other end, it's your turn. Go for it. We first saw this bridge on a pleasant day in 1989, and the scenery was inspiring.

Seattle in the Round

Our drive back into Washington State takes us through Seattle. Recently, we stayed at the his-toric Vance Hotel, rode the monorail from downtown Seattle to Seattle Center, and enjoyed breakfast in the Space Needle Restaurant.

We have fond memories of one September day when we enjoyed an anniversary dinner at this restaurant. Despite our initial disappointment when told window tables were not available for just two people, we got smart and shared a table with another couple. The four of us got acquainted as we watched Seattle, the ferries and ships on Puget Sound, and the beautiful panorama pass in front of us as the restaurant revolved. I was so engrossed in visiting and gazing that I set my camera on the window ledge, which does not revolve, and later realized that the camera had stayed behind. I had to go back several tables to retrieve it.

3. Gray's River Bridge, Washington, 1990

3   *The Case of the Missing Bridge*

Gray's River Bridge (47-35-01), one-half mile southeast of the town of Gray's River, Washington, just off Washington State Highway 4. Built in 1905 with two Howe Truss spans of Gray's River and a length of 158 feet.

Gray's River Bridge was sixty-six years old when it was placed on the National Register of Historic Places in 1971. We visited the bridge in the 1970s and again in 1982. The bridge's age showed as the center crib pier of logs and boulders had settled and the bridge sagged slightly.

Restoration was underway when our son Milton visited the site in 1988. The plan was to complete the restoration in 1989, Washington State's centennial year. Elizabeth and I visited the site on July 26, 1989, and discovered that the bridge had vanished. New concrete piers, steel girders, and scaffolding occupied the place where the bridge had been. The only evidence of the Gray's River Bridge was the curved metal roof sections piled on the site.

Work on the project was considerably behind schedule. But all good things come to those who wait and make another, more timely, trip. The bridge had reappeared in May of 1990, looking new and strong, sitting on the new pier and steel girders. Its appearance had changed, but it was still a unique bridge with a curved, corrugated metal roof and shed roofs at the portals. It was still the Gray's River Bridge.

The Colfax/Road Bridge and the Ashnola River Road Bridge are supported by the Howe Truss, patented by William Howe. Wooden beams cross to form an X with two beams in one direction and one in the opposite direction sandwiched in between. Vertical iron rods between each set of wooden beams add rigidity to the structure. We could not see these trusses at the first two bridges because of the siding, but we are able to see them at the Gray's River Bridge.

Our trip continues east on Washington State Highway 4 to Interstate 5 and south toward Vancouver, Washington.

Howe Truss, Gray's River Bridge

B1   *Introducing the Bonus Bridge*

Lynch/Grist Mill/Cedar Creek Bridge (47-06-02) east of Woodland, Washington, an 83-foot long Howe Truss span of Cedar Creek built in 1995.

The covered bridges numbered 1 to 100 are those that Elizabeth and I have seen and chosen to include on our tour. We have added other bridges that are important, interesting, or just fun. Some of these bridges we have seen. Others we haven't, but we wanted to let our readers know about them anyway. In this book, we call them "bonus bridges."

Lynch/Grist Mill/Cedar Creek Bridge, a new structure north of Vancouver, Washington, is situated next to a historic gristmill. The mill dates back to 1876, and the bridge to 1995. Cedar Creek cascades down beside the mill and flows under the bridge. Tourists can occasionally see grain being ground at the mill as water from Cedar Creek flows through a flume to power the machinery.

The bridge and mill can be reached by taking the Woodland exit from Interstate 5 north of Vancouver, immediately crossing Lewis River, going east nine miles on Cedar Creek Road, and one mile north on Grist Road.

B1. Lynch/Grist Mill/Cedar Creek Bridge, Washington, 2002

4. Larwood Bridge, Oregon, 1982

20

4   *Born in Covered Bridge Country*

Larwood Bridge (37-22-06) east of Crabtree, Oregon. Crosses Crabtree Creek. Built in 1939 with a 105-foot Western Howe Truss.

Our route takes us south on Interstate 5 into Oregon. We exit east from Albany, go one and one-half miles east of Crabtree, and continue east eight miles to the Larwood Bridge on Fish Hatchery Road. Roaring River, a small but lively stream, cascades down to quieter waters where Crabtree Creek flows under the bridge. The setting is a wayside park with a small footbridge, and the park provides many opportunities to photograph the bridge, river, and creek from both sides of the water—or from the water if you are careless.

The bridge has siding and a roof, but most of the sides are open. The interior trusses are protected from direct rainfall by the roof, but the trusses may get wet at times from a driving rain. The Howe Truss, visible from inside or outside, is a variation known as the Western Howe Truss, made with diagonal wood beams in one direc-

tion and crossed beams in the center panel only.

We are in Linn County. I was born here in Scio, Oregon, in 1920 and went to grade school at Stayton, ten miles north. There are twelve covered bridges in the county, all younger than I am. We tracked down the Larwood Bridge and six other nearby bridges in 1982.

The opportunity exists to find these bridges all in one day if you have a list, available at tourist centers, or a copy of the World Guide to Covered Bridges published by the National Society for the Preservation of Covered Bridges.

 5   *The Village Bridge*

Chitwood Bridge (37-21-03) at Chitwood, Oregon, crosses the Yaquina River with a 96-foot Howe Truss span. Built in 1930, rehabilitated in 1984.

We return west to Albany, cross Interstate 5, and continue through Albany on U.S. 20 to the

5. Chitwood Bridge, Oregon, 1988

Ocean at Yachats, Oregon, 1985

village of Chitwood. Just to the left we see the Chitwood Bridge, the village, and the railroad tracks compressed into a charming scene.

Chitwood was once a thriving town, with stores, a telephone office, a dance hall, and a few homes. When the sandstone and lumber industries died, so did the town. The bridge was fifty-two years old when we first saw it in 1982. The siding had weathered to a silver-gray. On our next visit, in 1988, we found the bridge painted red, an unexpected change.

Yachats: The Town and the Bridge

North Fork, Yachats River Bridge (37-21-08), with 42 foot Howe Truss built in 1938.

Elizabeth and I first met at the Service Center in Hancock, Michigan, fell in love, and were married in 1944. She was pretty, small, and charming. When my furlough came, we rode the train night and day by coach to Portland, Oregon, and Betty and my parents met. She was her natural self and got acquainted easily. I think my father was smitten. The four of us drove to the Oregon coast and Betty saw the Pacific Ocean for the first time.

In 1982, the Oregon coast was just ahead, a magnet that attracted us if we were anywhere near. We were drawn by the beauty, the feeling of awe and mystery, and the many opportunities for sightseeing, walking the beach, getting our feet wet, and beachcombing. Following dinner at our favorite restaurant in Yachats, we returned to the motel to watch the restless ocean and to listen to it as darkness hid it from our view.

Yachats (Ya-hots) is our favorite spot for watching the energy of the ocean. We are intrigued by the waves crashing against the rocky shoreline and we photograph them, expecting the next wave to be bigger and better. We always end up with entirely too many photos.

The North Fork of the Yachats River extends inland from town. A pleasant nine-mile drive on the Yachats River Road takes us to the North Fork, Yachats River Bridge. The weathered structure blends into the deep shade at this location.

B2. North Fork, Yachats River Bridge, Oregon, 1982

 A Bridge Adrift

Upper Drift Creek Bridge (37-21-14) built in 1914 across Upper Drift Creek, rebuilt in 2001 across Bear Creek near Otis, Oregon. A 66-foot Howe Truss span.

Betty and I visited Upper Drift Creek Bridge north of Newport not far from Lincoln City in 1982. The bridge was closed and deteriorating. The Lincoln County Commissioners decided in 1997 that the bridge should be demolished. Our son Milton sent us a news item from the Eugene Register Guard with this sad news. Laura and Kerry Sweitz persuaded the commissioners to let them take the bridge, replace the rotted timbers, and relocate it to their property. The bridge would remain county property and be accessible to the public. The deal was struck, and after four

years and a lot of help, with moments of frustration, despair, and elation, the Sweitzes succeeded.

In 2002, Milton and I found the relocated bridge eight miles north of its original site, now across Bear Creek near Otis. To find it, exit Oregon State Highway 18 between Rose Lodge and Otis, take Drift Creek Falls Trail Road, and drive one mile south to the bridge.

 Taming the Wildcat

Wildcat Bridge (37-20-04) east of Mapleton, Oregon. A 75-foot Howe Truss built across Wildcat Creek in 1925.

In 1993, Betty and I hoped to see Wildcat

[Above] B3. Upper
Drift Creek Bridge,
Oregon, 2002

[At right] 6. Wildcat
Bridge, Oregon, 1993

7. Goodpasture Bridge, Oregon, 1993

Bridge. On two previous occasions, we had failed to find it.

Continuing south on U.S. 101 to Florence, we head inland on Oregon State Highway 126, following the directions given in the World Guide to Covered Bridges. Beginning at Mapleton, we keep a careful count of the miles. We travel twelve miles to Siuslaw Road, which is just at the end of the highway bridge across the Siuslaw River, then go right, double back under the highway to Austa Road, and soon find the bridge where it crosses Wildcat Creek.

Finding Wildcat Bridge is a reward in itself, but it is also a bridge to admire. It has a long, narrow opening on one side and a picturesque setting on Wildcat Creek where the creek enters the Siuslaw River. Wildcat Bridge is on Stagecoach Road, formerly a highway extending from this point, through Swisshome, and continuing to Florence.

7   *Weekends on the McKenzie River*

Goodpasture Bridge (37-20-10) at Vida, Oregon. Built in 1938 with one 165-foot Howe Truss span of the McKenzie River.

Oregon State Highway 126 continues east through Eugene and Springfield along the McKenzie River. In 1946, this river called me away from classes at the University of Oregon and Betty away from homemaking in our trailer in Eugene. We caught some sun, read, watercolored, and loafed. Later, in 1965, we saw and photographed the Goodpasture Bridge where it crosses the McKenzie River at Vida.

This beautiful bridge, with a 165-foot, single span, can be seen by travelers along the McKenzie River Highway between Eugene and Bend. The bridge sits high above the river on concrete piers. Ten rectangular louvered openings on each side provide light and ventilation to the bridge

Betty and Frank at McKenzie River, Oregon, 1946

interior while deflecting the rain. The openings are cut off diagonally at the upper corners where the wood Howe Truss members cross. Goodpasture Bridge is well maintained, in continual use, and sturdy enough for logging trucks. It looked the same to us in 1982 and 1993 as it had in 1965.

 Last Covered Railroad Bridge in Oregon

Chambers Railroad Bridge (37-20-40) in Cottage Grove, Oregon. The bridge crosses the Coast Fork of the Willamette River with a 78-foot Howe Truss span built in 1936.

Covered bridges located in the vicinity of Eugene, Springfield, and Cottage Grove are not discussed on this tour. We do include the old, abandoned Chambers Railroad Bridge, the last

covered railroad bridge in Oregon as a bonus bridge. The Chambers Railroad Bridge was in use until 1943 on a spur line used for bringing logs to a sawmill in Cottage Grove. The bridge has a tall profile with the deck several feet above street level. When we saw it in 1990, the siding was mostly gone, leaving the large wooden beams and the triple iron rods of the Howe Truss plainly visible.

 Sunny Valley

Sunny Valley Bridge (37-17-01) built in 1920 with a 105-foot Howe Truss crossing of Grave Creek at Sunny Valley, Oregon.

Before Interstate 5 crossed Oregon from north to south, U.S. Highway 99 was a two-lane highway that resulted in a long and tedious journey.

8. Sunny Valley Bridge, Oregon, 1977

Several covered bridges existed along U.S. 99. Today, the bridge at Sunny Valley is the only one left along that route.

The Sunny Valley Bridge can be seen from Interstate 5. We have visited the bridge several times, and friends and relatives, knowing of our interest, have also stopped and sent us their photos. To visit the bridge, take the Sunny Valley exit on I-5 and drive one-half mile.

The bridge is 105 feet long. Vertical iron rods extend through the centers of the rectangular openings along each side. A large historical landmark sign at the bridge describes the death of a fourteen-year-old girl, a member of the first wagon train to travel the old Applegate Trail, and the deaths of five Indians, all buried in the same grave. The name Grave Creek derives from this bit of history. The bridge was originally known as Grave Creek Bridge, but the present, more cheerful name, suits me fine.

9 · A New Life for an Old Bridge

Antelope Creek Bridge (37-15-02), a 58-foot Queenpost Truss built in 1922, now located across Little Butte Creek in Eagle Point, Oregon.

Our first serious venture into covered bridge hunting occurred in 1982 and originated at the home of my sister Naomi and her husband Glen

9 Antelope Creek Bridge, Oregon, 1988

10. Honey Run Bridge, California, 1990

in Ashland, Oregon. After visiting with them for a couple of days and helping Glen chop their winter's supply of oak and madrone for firewood, we went looking for covered bridges.

The Antelope Creek Bridge, north of Medford and east of Eagle Point, seemed forlorn in 1982 as it stood at its remote location, bypassed, unused, and half-buried in weeds and brush. Six years later, we found the bridge again. It had been moved to the town of Eagle Point to provide a safe way for school children to cross Little Butte Creek. The old bridge had been remodeled with the addition of openings in the sides to allow daylight in plus electric lights for night. The site is attractively landscaped.

The siding, replaced in 2002, now covers the window openings, so the bridge is closer to its original appearance. The Queenpost Truss, with a horizontal beam at the center and diagonal beams sloping down to each end, is the first with this type of support on our tour. The diagrams on page 10 include a sketch of the Queenpost Truss, the Howe Truss, and the other types of trusses.

Three Roofs Over One River

Honey Run Bridge (05-04-01) with three spans (two Pratt Truss and one Kingpost Truss) and a total length of 230 feet. Built in 1896 across Butte Creek near Chico, California.

We rejoin Interstate 5 and head south into California, to Red Bluff, then on California State Highway 99 to Chico. Past Chico, about one and one-half miles past California 32, we exit east on Skyway Road, travel one and one-half miles to Honey Run Road, and go left four and one-half miles to the bridge.

Honey Run Bridge is most interesting, with three roof levels, like three bridges end to end. The bridge crosses Butte Creek, which is wide and wild when the flow of water is heavy. The

Honey Run Bridge is on the road from Chico to Paradise, was built in 1894, and was washed out and replaced in 1896. Today, it is like new with new siding and a new look.

The taller, longer center span has a Pratt Truss, with crossed diagonal iron rods and vertical wood beams. The longer of the end spans also uses the Pratt Truss. The shorter end span has a Kingpost Truss, a triangle of wood beams plus a vertical kingpost at the center. The diagrams on page 10 illustrate these two truss types. The new vertical siding is translucent with gaps between boards, and the bridge is bright and cheerful inside.

Longest of Its Kind

Bridgeport Bridge (05-29-01) located north of Nevada City, California, has a single 208-foot Howe Truss and Arch span of the South Fork of the Yuba River. Built in 1862 to replace an earlier toll bridge.

We return to California 99, go south to California 20 at Marysville, and east to Nevada City.

Sometimes, finding a covered bridge is half the fun. Bridgeport Bridge is worth finding. We drive north out of Nevada City on California 49 for eleven and one-half miles, then left for seven miles on Pleasant Valley Road to the bridge where it crosses the South Fork of the Yuba River. Finding it is not as difficult as it sounds. As we cross the river on a modern, new bridge, the long covered bridge is fully visible just upstream.

The exterior appearance of the Bridgeport Bridge is remarkable. Huge arches extend up from below the deck nearly to the roof. The exterior shakes outline these arches. Inside the bridge, we see the arched timbers measuring five by fourteen inches. The truss and the arch work together to support this great length and make this the longest single-span covered bridge in America.

11. Bridgeport Bridge, California, 1990

We stop overnight in Nevada City, view the local history on display at the museum in the old firehouse, and look through genealogical records.

Elizabeth's ancestors were tin miners in Cornwall County, England. Many immigrated to Michigan, Colorado, and perhaps to the Nevada mining areas. In 1990, we searched for familiar Cornish surnames in those genealogical records.

"There are too many Richard Rowes, William Williams, Joseph Hockings. How am I supposed to know if any are my relatives?"

First names reappear frequently in Cornish families. Elizabeth's name was passed down from grandmother to mother to daughter, and Elizabeth takes pride in her name. However, friends and family call her Betty, so Betty she will be from time to time in this narrative.

12

The Milton Graton Touch at Knight's Ferry

Knight's Ferry Bridge (05-50-01) built in 1864 with four Howe Truss spans and a total length of 330 feet where it crosses the Stanislaus River at Knight's Ferry, California.

We continue south from Nevada City to Stockton, then head east on California 120 looking for Knight's Ferry Bridge. It is one-half mile north of the highway, at the east end of the town of Knight's Ferry. The bridge is 330 feet long, with four spans, and is impressive as seen from the bank of the Stanislaus River. We view the length, the massive stone pier supports, and the portals at each end, which are painted with contrasting white and reddish-brown colors.

The old ferry at Knight's Ferry was replaced by a bridge in 1854. That bridge lasted until 1862 when it was washed out by floodwaters. The

12. Knight's Ferry Bridge and its portal [below], California, 1990

replacement, completed in 1864, was built eight feet higher, a precaution that has paid off. The bridge was closed in 1981 when it became unsafe for vehicles. Milton Graton, a renowned covered bridge expert, was called in and rehabilitated the bridge with the help of his sons and grandsons. Their work was completed in 1989. When we saw it in 1990, it was sparkling fresh with new paint and new siding. The bridge is structurally sound, although it is no longer used for traffic. Instead, it is preserved in a parklike setting.

 Covered Bridge at Yosemite

Wawona Bridge (05-22-01) was built before 1875 and covered in 1875, with the roof placed high to accommodate hay wagons. The bridge is 130 feet long, supported by a Queenpost Truss span of the South Fork of the Merced River. It is at the town of Wawona near the south entrance to Yosemite National Park.

Our tour in the West has included twelve covered bridges and our route has covered approximately nineteen hundred miles. It is not much further to Yosemite National Park. We had intended to continue to the park in 1990 to find the Wawona covered bridge at the southern end of the park, but canceled our plans because we chose to avoid the Memorial Day weekend traffic going to Yosemite.

We return to Sacramento, then head east on Interstate 80. We have a nineteen hundred-mile drive ahead to Winterset, Iowa, with no covered bridges in between.

Interstate 80 takes us through Reno, Salt Lake City, Cheyenne, and Omaha with many attractions along the way. In 1990, we drove south from Cheyenne to Central City, Colorado where Elizabeth's father, uncle, aunts, and grandparents lived before she was born. We continued south to Denver and, in the public library, found an 1897 Gilpin County Directory which included Central City.

"There's my dad, Richard Rowe Jr., dairyman. He was sixteen years old and he drove a team of horses and a wagon delivering milk. There's my uncle William O. Rowe, bartender. I don't remember anyone telling me he was a bartender. There are my aunts, Annie and Mamie, clerks." Later, in Hancock, Michigan, Annie and Mamie had established their own business, the Rowe Sisters Shop. "There's grandpa, Richard Rowe Sr., miner." The directory didn't list grandma, Mary Ann, because she was not a wage earner. She kept the house on High Street in Central City, keeping the family together while the others earned enough money to survive.

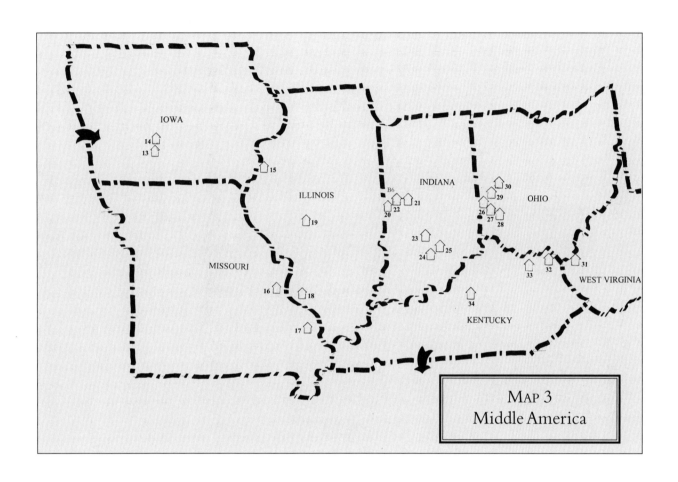

IOWA

14
13

15

ILLINOIS

19

MISSOURI

16   18

17

B6   INDIANA
22   21
20

23
24   25

26   30
27   29   OHIO
28

33   32   31

WEST VIRGINIA

34

KENTUCKY

MAP 3
Middle America

13. Holliwell Bridge, Iowa, 1989

Chapter Three

MIDDLE AMERICA

 Prairie Profiles

Holliwell Bridge (15-61-05), Winterset, Iowa, built in 1880 across the Middle River, with a single 122-foot Town Lattice Truss and Arch span.

Continuing east on Interstate 80, we leave the Interstate at DeSoto, Iowa, and drive south on U.S. 169 to Winterset, Iowa. Maps and directions to the several covered bridges in Madison County are available at Winterset. We are including the Holliwell and Roseman/Oak Grove bridges on this tour. Holliwell Bridge is east of Winterset on Iowa State Highway 92 and south on Scott Township Road. Roseman/Oak Grove Bridge is west of Winterset on Iowa 92 and south on Webster Township Road.

The Holliwell Bridge has a flat roof and a distinctive style common to several Madison County bridges. The flat roof seems appropriate for the level Iowa countryside. The roof and siding enclose and protect the Town Lattice Truss. "Town" is for Ithiel Town, the architect who patented the design in 1820, and "lattice" is because the diagonal beams cross to resemble a lattice. Benton Jones, the builder, added arched beams. Wooden pegs and iron bars tie the truss and arch into a unified structure. The diagonal braces between the ceiling and the sides are intended to keep the bridge from leaning sideways. In 1989, Holliwell Bridge had a pronounced sideways lean, so the bracing was not completely effective. Restoration in 1995 corrected the structural problem.

Roseman/Oak Grove Bridge (15-61-07), built in 1883, crosses Middle River, Winterset, Iowa, with a 107-foot Town Lattice and Queenpost Truss span.

In 1989, the Roseman/Oak Grove Bridge was in need of attention. The county renovated it in 1992, around the same time that the novel *The Bridges of Madison County* was published. The book, a huge success, was scheduled to become a movie. Because Roseman Bridge was important in the story, it was also a key location in the movie. The renovated bridge looked too new for the 1965 time period, so the movie technicians artificially "aged" it by removing some siding and making the paint look as though it was peeling. They "removed" the aging in 1995, and the bridge has presumably aged naturally since then.

Cedar/Casper Bridge (15-61-03), also included in the book and the movie, was severely damaged by fire in 2002. A covered bridge festival takes place in Winterset each October, making October a good time to visit the bridges of Madison County.

We travel south and east to Burlington, Iowa. When we stop at the Welcome Center at the Port of Burlington, we hear of Snake Alley, a block-long, one-way, steep serpentine roadway. It is easy to find and fun to drive, similar to Lombard Street in San Francisco but without the congestion.

14. Roseman/Oak Grove Bridge, Iowa, 1989

Snake Alley, Burlington, Iowa, 1995

15. Allaman/Eames Bridge, Illinois, 1995

15

Round Trip Across the Mississippi River

Allaman/Eames Bridge (13-36-01), built in 1865, rebuilt in 1984. A 106-foot Burr Truss span of Henderson Creek, in a roadside park near Gladstone, Illinois.

Crossing the Mississippi River from Burlington, Iowa on U.S. 34, across the new bridge to Illinois State Highway 164, we drive north three and one-half miles to Allaman/Eames Bridge located in a park on the right side of the highway.

The Allaman/Eames Bridge is one of the few remaining covered bridges in Illinois out of more than one hundred that once existed. The bridges were disappearing at an alarming rate when authorities decided to preserve the ones that remained. Jacob Allaman built the Allaman/Eames Bridge in 1865 for $2,125. It carried traffic across Henderson Creek on a 106-foot Burr Truss span. The bridge was in use until 1934 when it was acquired from the county by the Illinois State Division of Highways and was preserved as the main feature of the roadside park where it is located.

In 1982, Henderson Creek flooded, lifting the bridge off its abutments and carrying it downstream where it lodged against a highway bridge near Oquawka. Local citizens, the Henderson County Historical Society, and the Illinois State Department of Transportation worked together to raise the money needed to return the bridge to its upstream location and to rebuild it. The bridge was rebuilt using mostly salvaged original timbers. It was elevated three and one-half feet in 1984, and so far that has been high enough. We found the bridge in excellent condition in 1995, attractive with red horizontal siding.

Our route returns to Burlington, Iowa, goes south on U.S. 61 to St. Louis, Missouri. Many attractions and opportunities for sightseeing are available along this route including Hannibal, Missouri, the home of Mark Twain. At the Gateway Arch in St. Louis, and in the company of our daughter Susan, we rode the tramway part of the way and climbed the rest of the way to the top of the Arch in 1991. We peered through the small openings toward the west, and then eastward toward Illinois, Indiana, and Ohio. This is where our tour is headed . But first there are covered bridges to be seen in Missouri.

 16 *Study in Red and Green*

Sandy Creek/LeMay Ferry Road Bridge (25-50-01), a 76-foot Howe Truss span of Sandy Creek built in 1886 on the old LeMay Ferry Road between Hillsboro and St. Louis, Missouri.

We drive south of St. Louis on Missouri State Highway 21, looking for the Sandy Creek/LeMay Ferry Road Bridge four and one-half miles north of Hillsboro. If we find ourselves at Hillsboro, we have gone too far and must go back north for four and one-half miles, then go east one-half mile to the bridge.

Sandy Creek/LeMay Ferry Road Bridge straddles the creek in a wooded setting alive with reds and greens. The deep red of the bridge and the lighter reddish color of the gravel at the approaches contrast with the bright green foliage. The original covered bridge, built of white pine for $2,000, was destroyed by floodwater and was replaced in 1886 by the present bridge.

 17 *The Bridge at the Mill*

Bollinger Mill Bridge (25-16-01) crosses the Whitewater River at the mill near Burfordville, Missouri. Built in 1868 with a 140-foot Howe Truss span.

We return south to Hillsboro, go east to Interstate 55, then south to Missouri State Highway 34 and west to Jackson and Burfordville. Bollinger Mill and Bollinger Mill Bridge are at the edge of Burfordville.

Major George Frederick Bollinger received a land grant of 640 acres here in 1797. He fought in the War of 1812, built Bollinger Mill, and brought twenty families from North Carolina to settle the area. The mill was burned by Union troops in 1864 and was rebuilt by Major Bollinger in 1867. It is a four-story, water-powered, horizontal grist mill. The bridge, started in 1860, was completed in 1868. The Missouri Highway Department restored it in 1950. Both the mill and the bridge are well maintained. The setting on the Whitewater River at the low dam is superb and provides an excellent opportunity for photographs.

 18 *Toll No More*

Little Mary's River Bridge (13-79-01) built in 1854. A 98-foot Burr Truss spans the Little Mary's River near Chester, Illinois.

Not far away is another covered bridge near Chester, Illinois. Returning east from Burfordsville to Interstate 65, we drive north to exit on Missouri State Highway 51, go north and cross the Mississippi River to Chester. Little Mary's River Bridge is located four and one-half miles north on Illinois State Highway 150 in a park on the east side of the highway.

It was a pleasant day in May of 1991 when Elizabeth and I enjoyed a leisurely stroll around Little Mary's River Bridge in the park. The

16. Sandy Creek/LeMay Ferry Road Bridge, Missouri, 1991

17. Bollinger Mill Bridge, Missouri, 1991

18. Little Mary's River Bridge, Illinois, 1991

bridge, built in 1854, was originally on a planked toll road that ran between Chester and Bremen, and was in continuous use until 1930 when it was retired from service. The Chester Chamber of Commerce raised money to rehabilitate the bridge. Illinois acquired the bridge and site, added steel beams below the deck to forestall collapse of the structure, and replaced the siding and roof with new wood.

A plaque on the bridge explains it all. "Mary's River Covered Bridge. Built 1854. Continuous service 1854 to 1930. Was originally part of a planked toll road between Bremen and Chester. All of the timber in this bridge is the original, with the exceptions of the floor, floor joists, roof and siding. Acquired by the State of Illinois in 1936 for purposes of preservation and as a picnic area. Money for purchase donated by Chester Chamber of Commerce."

19 *Light Weight and Heavily Used*

Glenarm/Hedley/Sugar Creek Bridge (13-84-02) near Glenarm, Illinois, spans Sugar Creek with a 58-foot Multiple Kingpost and Arch Truss. Built about 1880, in use until 1984.

We head north toward Springfield, Illinois, take exit 83 from Interstate 55, head west one mile, and then right one mile.

The Glenarm/Hedley/Sugar Creek Bridge enjoys a quiet spot, even though it is close to Interstate 55 and adjacent to an area in transition from rural to suburban. We wonder and wander a bit before looking past the modern suburbs to discover the bridge and its rural setting across the street, more or less, from the homes.

In 1963, the Illinois Legislature passed the law requiring that remaining covered bridges be

19. Glenarm/Hedley/Sugar Creek Bridge, Illinois, 1989

saved. At the time, the Glenarm/Hedley/Sugar Creek Bridge was in sad condition with missing guardrails and loose and missing siding. Illinois decided to save this bridge as its first project under the new law. The bridge was rebuilt without compromising its original appearance. Even the sag, a tribute to its age and ability to survive, remains. When we saw the bridge in 1989 after it had been restored, it was like stepping back in time one hundred years. We trust it will continue to retain its timeless charm.

Our tour takes us north to Springfield, then north and east to Danville, Illinois. Danville was a convenient stop at the end of a long day of travel in 1992. We were at a motel with the Vermillion River on one side and a restaurant on the other. As sunset approached, Elizabeth and I were tempted by the notion of a chocolate milk shake, so we headed out of the motel. Several hot air

balloons were floating overhead into the sunset. I scrambled back to our room for my camera and managed to get some photos. We learned that Danville hosts the Oldsmobile Balloon Classic in Illinois each June, but we were there in July, so these balloons must have been stragglers.

Later, as I was sitting in the car holding my milk shake in one hand and reaching for something in the back seat with the other, I managed to spill some of my milk shake on our travel literature, in particular a National Geographic guide printed on slick paper. There was an unfortunate chemical reaction which cemented some of the pages together. I don't remember what I said, or what Betty said, and that is fortunate. I would just as soon forget the unexpected milk shake fiasco and remember the pleasure of seeing the hot air balloons.

20 *Long and Narrow*

Newport Bridge (14-83-04) near Newport, Indiana, built 1885 with a 205-foot Burr Truss span of Little Vermillion River about four miles above its confluence with the Wabash River.

Indiana and Vermillion County are just east of Danville. The county is about twenty-five miles long, and five to ten miles wide. Within this narrow strip, sandwiched between the Illinois/Indiana border and the Wabash River, we find three covered bridges. One, the Newport Bridge, is included in our tour.

Our route is south on Indiana State Highway 63 to Indiana 71, west one-half mile and left one-half mile. Newport Bridge, built in1885, is 205 feet long. The four long arches in each Burr Truss reach to the ceiling and extend below the deck into the abutments. The portal openings at each end of Newport Bridge are arched at the top. The metal roof has a slight reddish hue.

B6 *Eugene Bridge*

Eugene Bridge (14-83-05), a single 212-foot long Burr Truss span of Big Vermillion River built in 1885. Located at Eugene, Indiana.

Eugene Bridge is a few miles north and is the same age and slightly longer than Newport Bridge. It has two arches in each Burr Truss,

Burr Truss, Newport Bridge

20. Newport Bridge, Indiana, 1992

21. Narrows Bridge, Indiana, 1989

another subtle difference from Newport Bridge.

Hillsdale Bridge (14-83-03) is to the south at Dana, in Ernie Pyle Park. The restored home of famed World War II correspondent, Ernie Pyle, is at Dana.

Our tour returns to Indiana State Highway 63, south to U.S. 36, and east to Rockville, Indiana.

Five Tours Out of Rockville

Parke County, Indiana, hosts a covered bridge festival each October, with many activities including conducted tours. The information and tour center is in a former railroad depot at Rockville, the county seat. This is the starting point for five covered bridge tours shown on maps and identified by markers as the red, brown, blue, black and

yellow routes. Each tour includes a significant portion of the thirty-two covered bridges in the county. In May of 1989, we located a few of the Parke County bridges on our own and include two from the blue route on our trip.

 Bookends

Narrows Bridge (14-61-36) built in 1882 with a 141-foot Burr Truss span of Sugar Creek at the east end of Turkey Run State Park, Indiana.

Driving north from Rockville, we expect to find two covered bridges in Turkey Run State Park. The attendant at the park entrance advises us that the bridges are not in the park, but are located on the east and west sides adjacent to the

43

22. Cox Ford Bridge, Indiana, 1989

park. We continue east from the park entrance on Indiana State Highway 47 for three-quarters of a mile, then left three-quarters of a mile.

The Narrows Bridge, built in 1882 by J.A. Britton, provided access to the Lusk Mill. A concrete bridge replaced the covered bridge in 1960, bypassing the old bridge. The Narrows Bridge is a part of a scenic setting where Sugar Creek passes through a rocky narrows. The bridge was being painted when we photographed it in 1989.

Cox Ford Bridge (14-61-34), a 192-foot Burr Truss span of Sugar Creek at the west end of Turkey Run State Park, Indiana, built in 1913.

Driving back past the park entrance to the west edge of the park and then three-quarters of a mile to the right, we find the Cox Ford Bridge. The bridge is placed high above the water, probably in the hope it will not be taken out by flood, as was the iron bridge at this location that was destroyed in 1912. The stream banks slope down to the water.

While enjoying a tailgate-style lunch at our car in 1989, we watched as a group of people arrived, launched a canoe, and paddled east, perhaps to enjoy the rock gorges in the park and at the Narrows Bridge. We liked the impressive look of the long bridge set high above the water. It was startling the first time we saw Cox Ford Bridge on TV in a brief piece on Charles Kuralt's America when his recreational vehicle emerged from our bridge.

44

A New Sound

Ramp Creek Bridge (14-07-02), a 110-foot long, double-barreled Burr Truss built in 1838 across Ramp Creek near Fincastle. Now crosses Salt Creek at the entrance to Brown County State Park, Indiana.

The route south and east from Turkey Run State Park to Bloomington goes near Fincastle. In 1838, a two lane covered bridge was built across Ramp Creek, on a highway between Lafayette to the north and New Albany to the south. The road was busy and catered to horse-and-buggy traffic. The clippity clop of horse's hooves must have taken on a special timbre inside the bridge. Times change. In 1932, the bridge was dismantled and moved to the entrance to Brown County State Park, east of Bloomington. We saw the bridge in 1989. It was still heavily used, but resounded with the rumble of autos as they crossed the bridge to enter or leave the park.

A third truss between the twelve-foot-wide traffic lanes can be seen through the white portals at each end of the bridge. Ramp Creek

Bridge, painted red on the sides, seems much longer when viewed from the side than it does when viewed head-on. The brown-shingled roof adds a third color.

There's More of Medora

Medora Bridge (14-36-04) built in 1875, crosses the East Fork of the White River with three Burr Truss spans and a total length of 459 feet. Located near Medora, Indiana.

The town of Medora is off U.S. 50 east of Bedford, Indiana. Although the Medora Bridge is out of town, and on a section of Indiana 235 that has been bypassed, it is not easily hidden. The bridge stretches across the East Fork of the White River with three spans and a total length of 459 feet. The bridge has red siding and a gray roof, and sits atop piers and abutments above the fast-running, chocolate-brown river water. Viewed from the

23. Ramp Creek Bridge, Indiana, 1989

24. Medora Bridge, Indiana, 1989

outside, the bridge stretches across the width of our photo. Inside, the three sets of arches gradually diminish toward the distant portal. This is the longest covered bridge supported by the Burr Truss in the United States.

25 The Last of Its Kind

Bell's Ford Bridge (14-36-03) built in 1869 with a two-span Post Truss and a length of 330 feet. Crosses the East Fork of the White River near Seymour, Indiana.

Not far from Medora is our next covered bridge. We drive east and north to Brownstown and east on U.S. 50 about seven miles to Sixth Street, west of downtown Seymour. Bell's Ford Bridge is immediately to the north on a section of Indiana 258 that has been bypassed.

Bell's Ford Bridge, like Medora Bridge, crosses the East Fork of the White River. The bridge,

with two spans and a total length of 330 feet, was built in 1869. It is the only covered bridge remaining in America with the Post Truss. This truss has wooden beams set at steep angles and a criss-crossing network of iron rods. Simeon S. Post, the designer, was an inventor and railroad engineer. While his patented bridge trusses were usually made entirely of iron, the design could be adapted by combining wood beams with iron rods. The bridge is designed to be strong without using excess material—the bridge of an engineer. It is closed to vehicles, but a catwalk has been added so that tourists can go inside and view this unique truss.

26 Double-Wide on the Pike

Roberts Bridge (35-68-05) originally south of Eaton, Ohio, across Seven Mile Creek, now at Eaton. Built 1829, 79-foot long Burr Truss span (double-barreled).

25. Bell's Ford Bridge, Indiana, 1989

26. Roberts Bridge, Ohio, 1992

We go north to Interstate 70, then east into Ohio, and southeast on U.S. 35 to Eaton, looking for Roberts Bridge. It was built on the Camden Pike in 1829 with two lanes and a third truss between the two traffic lanes in order to accommodate the considerable traffic of horse-drawn vehicles. The bridge adapted to changing times as the Pike became U.S. 127 and motor vehicles replaced horses. Finally, it was bypassed. Unused and isolated, the bridge suffered severely from neglect and vandalism, and in 1986, was seriously damaged by arson. Strong sentiment to rebuild the bridge existed and considerable controversy about whether to rebuild it at its isolated location ensued. Relocation won out, and a safer home was found in a park in the town of Eaton.

This is where we found the bridge in 1992. Roberts Bridge is very attractive, with new horizontal siding, a new roof, and an essentially new inside. However, original structural members, charred from the arson, remain as part of the bridge. Steel beams have been added below the deck to help the old charred timbers support Roberts Bridge.

It was satisfying to find the Roberts Bridge restored. We relaxed, took a break, admired the bridge, and watched the ducks swim in the quiet waters above the low dam.

A Childs Bridge

Brubaker Bridge (35-68-06) built in 1887 with an 85-foot Childs Truss span of Sam's Run. Located near Gratis, Ohio.

Ohio has been the birthplace of several innovative bridge truss designs, patented in the names of the designers. Brubaker Bridge is a few miles southeast of Eaton and can be reached by Ohio State Highway 122, west on Ohio 725 for one-half mile, and right one-half mile.

Brubaker Bridge uses the Childs Truss. Horace Childs patented his truss in 1846. A significant feature of his design are the wide wooden beams

Burr Truss, damaged by arson, has been sandblasted.

shaped like planks. Each diagonal wooden plank is crossed by a diagonal iron rod. The truss as an integral part of the bridge structure is fully revealed by the open sides, which allow light into the interior. The white bridge with its gray shake roof is in an appealing green and wooded setting.

Upside Down in Germantown

Germantown Bridge (35-57-01), in Germantown, Ohio. Built in 1865 with a 100-foot Inverted Bowstring Arch. Crosses Little Twin Creek in town.

Returning to Ohio 725 and heading east takes us to Germantown. The Germantown Bridge is in town on East Center Street. It is supported by iron arches which extend down from the large corner posts to the deck at the center of the bridge. This is an Inverted Bowstring Arch, rare in covered bridges. Structural uniqueness aside, the Germantown Bridge is charming and photogenic.

This bridge, originally on the Dayton Pike, was moved to its present location in 1911. It was rebuilt in 1982, and looked fresh and new in 1992 when we visited. We thoroughly enjoyed seeing this bridge and took pictures we could treasure later.

27. Brubaker Bridge, Ohio, 1992

28. Germantown Bridge, Ohio, 1992

29. Dixon Branch Bridge, Ohio, 1989

A Model Bridge

Dixon Branch Bridge (35-68-04), 50 feet long, supported by a Childs Truss, built in 1887 on Concord Road where it crossed Dixon Branch Creek. Moved in 1964 to Civitan Park in Lewisburg, Ohio.

Lewisburg is west from Germantown on Ohio 725 and north on Ohio 503. We were here in 1989 looking for the Dixon Branch Bridge. We soon found it in Civitan Park. The bridge was moved from its original location across Dixon Branch Creek after it suffered wind damage, and was repaired and dedicated at its new location in 1964.

There was no water under the bridge, but there was lots of water around it on the day we visited, as it was raining heavily. I took a few pictures inside where it was dry, then stepped outside for a few quick shots. A gentleman came up

and engaged me in conversation. He had built a scale model of Dixon Branch Bridge and was telling me all about it. Elizabeth, sitting in our car, wondered why two grown men were standing out in the rain talking when they could have stayed dry under the bridge roof. The downpour persisted and we found a motel in Dayton. We used this unplanned break to visit the Montgomery County Historical Museum.

Long is Relative

Eldean Bridge (35-55-01) with a 225-foot Long Truss with two spans built in 1860. Spans the Great Miami River north of Troy, Ohio.

We head east from Lewisburg on I-70 and north on I-75 to Troy and north for two and one-quarter miles on County Road 25. Eldean Bridge is immediately to the right. The bridge faces a park, and a good front view of the bridge portal can be seen from the park. A good side view can be seen from the adjacent new bridge. The vertical siding is painted red and there are several small rectangular openings along the sides. The roof, which is white, extends out over the portal openings.

Eldean Bridge has two spans crossing the Great Miami River. The truss, a design by Stephen Long, has horizontal wood beams at the top and bottom, vertical wood beams dividing the truss into panels, and crossed diagonal wood beams within each panel. Colonel Long's truss, patented in 1830, was in demand for both road and railroad bridges. The Long Truss preceded the Howe Truss; the Howe Truss substituted vertical iron rods for the vertical wood beams. Eldean Bridge is the longest Long Truss covered bridge in America, except for one we'll see in New York State, which also adds an arch.

31 A Palette of Color

Milton/Sinks Mill Bridge (48-06-01) at Milton, West Virginia. Built in 1876 with a single 148-foot Howe Truss and Arch span of the Mud River. Renovated and relocated in 2002 to Milton Pumpkin Festival Park.

Our next destination is south and east from Troy to Portsmouth, Ohio, and on to Huntington, West Virginia, east on Interstate 64, take exit 28 to Milton Bridge.

We found the Milton/Sinks Mill Bridge sitting high above the Mud River. The span of 148 feet used the Howe Truss plus an arch. The bridge was in disrepair when we saw it in 1991. The red vertical siding, gray shingled roof, gray stone abutments, abundant greenery, and cocoa-colored river created a palette of color.

A ferry crossed the Mud River near here until 1834 when it was replaced by the covered bridge. This bridge was a vital crossing point for the Kenawha and James River Turnpike, with a stagecoach line operating on the turnpike from

30. Eldean Bridge, Ohio, 1992

31. Milton/Sink's Mill Bridge, West Virginia, 1991

1835 to 1873. The original covered bridge was replaced in 1876 by the present bridge. It was rebuilt and, in 2002, was relocated to the Milton Pumpkin Festival Park grounds about a mile from its original location. It now spans a pond instead of a river.

32 A Hop and a Jump

Oldtown Bridge (17-45-02) between Oldtown and Hopewell, Kentucky. Built 1870 with two Multiple Kingpost Truss spans totaling 188 feet across Little Sandy Creek.

It isn't much more than a hop and a jump to the Oldtown Bridge west of Milton and into Kentucky on Interstate 64 to Kentucky State Highway 1 near Grayson. We go north on Kentucky 1 to the Oldtown Bridge on the right. The location is between Hopewell and Oldtown.

The Oldtown Bridge has two spans in the 188-foot crossing of Little Sandy Creek—a 50-foot hop and a 138-foot jump. The Multiple Kingpost Truss worked well for the shorter span, but it has not been adequate for the longer span, which has developed a considerable sag.

The roof of the Oldtown Bridge, which extends out over the portals, combines with a continuous open strip between the roof and the siding to make it appear as if the roof is floating free above the rest of the bridge. We liked the way the bridge looked, even with the sag, and wondered if the two spans had been of equal length, would the bridge have been sturdier?

33 A Skip to Church

Goddard/White Bridge (17-35-06) at Goddard, Kentucky. A 63-foot Town Lattice Truss span of Sandlick Creek. Construction date not known.

32. Oldtown Bridge, Kentucky, 1991

Multiple Kingpost Truss, Oldtown Bridge

We return to Interstate 64, continue west and exit north at Kentucky State Highway 32 to Goddard, Kentucky.

The Goddard/White Bridge is a small, attractive covered bridge with vertical, weathered sid-

ing and a tin roof. The Town Lattice Truss members, joined by wooden pegs, can be seen inside the bridge. The crossing at Sandlick Creek is an open setting, so the Goddard/White Bridge can be viewed from all directions. The bridge was restored in 1968, and we found it to be well maintained in 1991. A small Methodist church is nearby. The church burned recently but has also been restored. Elizabeth captured our daughter Susan, and me in a photo of the bridge and its surroundings.

 34 *Two Arched Jumps*

Beech Fork/Mooresville Bridge (17-115-01) south of Chaplin, Kentucky. Built in 1865 with two Burr Truss spans and a 211 foot long crossing of the Beech Fork River.

Our route goes west on Interstate 64 and takes

33. Goddard/White Bridge, Kentucky, 1991

34. Beech Fork/Mooresville Bridge, Kentucky, 1991

us to Lexington, west out of Lexington on U.S. 60, and then southwest on the Blue Grass Parkway toward Bardstown and Elizabethtown. We exit on Kentucky State Highway 55, go south to Kentucky 468 at Mooresville, then north on 468 for two and one-half miles. The Beech Fork/Mooresville Bridge is on the left.

The Beech Fork/Mooresville Bridge has two spans of equal length using the Burr Truss, which is like the Multiple Kingpost Truss in Oldtown Bridge, but with an arch added. The added arch in Beech Fork/Mooresville Bridge contributes greatly to its strength, making it stronger than the Oldtown Bridge. The brownish tin roof of Beech Fork/Mooresville Bridge accents the gray weathered siding. The covered bridge has been bypassed, and a newer bridge is nearby.

In Kentucky, a sign at each bridge site describes the bridge and notes that the bridge is listed on the National Register of Historic Places. A separate sign titled Covered Bridges reads: "Covered bridges were first built in the 1790s but did not become widely popular until after 1814. They were covered to protect them from the weather. At one time there were more than 400 covered bridges in Ky. The timbered spans have played a romantic role in our history. Some were destroyed during Civil War. The remaining ones are a nostalgic link with the past."

It is startling to realize that only thirteen covered bridges remain in Kentucky of four hundred that are claimed to have been built. We can hope that these thirteen will be protected and preserved as a valued heritage.

We return to the Blue Grass Parkway and continue west through Bardstown to Elizabethtown, south on Interstate 65, past Mammoth Caves National Park, through Nashville, Tennessee, and continue to Cullman, Alabama. We have traveled about nineteen hundred miles in Middle America. From Cullman, we continue our covered bridge tour through the South and Southeast.

55

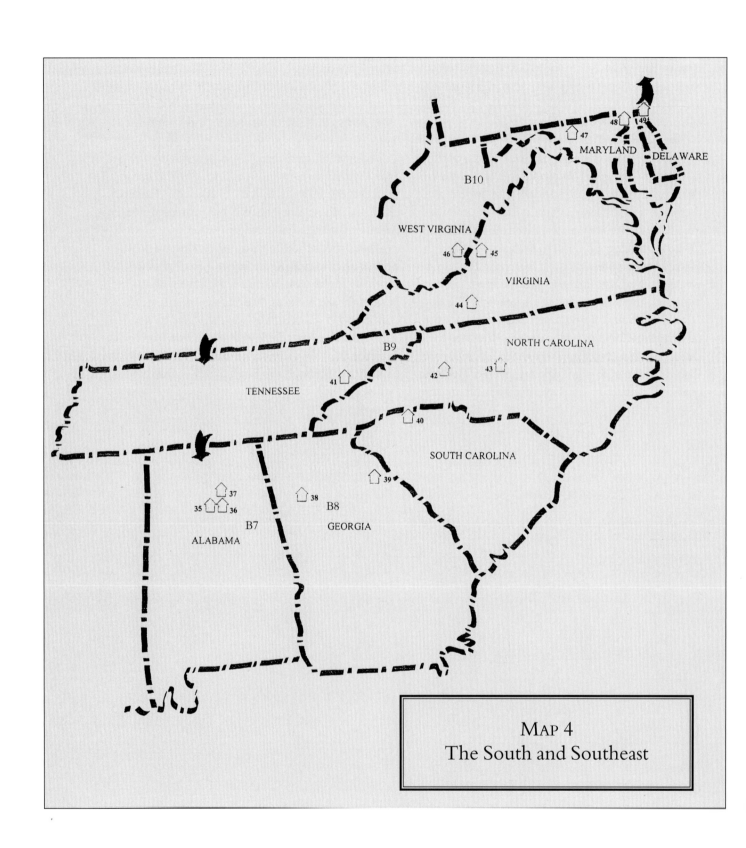

MAP 4
The South and Southeast

Chapter Four

THE SOUTH AND SOUTHEAST

35 *Still Young*

Swann/Joy Bridge (01-05-05), 320 feet in length. Crosses Locust Fork of the Black Warrior River with three Town Lattice Truss spans. Built in 1933, located at the edge of Cleveland, Alabama.

Elizabeth and I stayed overnight at Cullman, Alabama, in 1991, after driving many miles, blissfully unaware that it was the weekend of the Talladega races and that the motels were full. We were lucky to find a cancellation at Cullman and doubly lucky to be near three covered bridges.

Following a good night's sleep, we drive east from Cullman on U.S. 278 to U.S. 231 and south to Cleveland, then south three-quarters of a mile on Alabama State Highway 79 and one mile right to Swann/Joy Bridge.

Swann/Joy Bridge is long and high above the Locust Fork of the Black Warrior River. We are able to pull off the road and walk to a vantage point below the bridge to see and appreciate its length and height. We can see part of the Town Lattice Truss. Later, inside the bridge, while watching for traffic, we get a good look at the interior.

36 *Seventy and Counting*

Old Easley/Rosa Bridge (01-05-12) near Oneonta, Alabama. Built in 1927 with a 96-foot Town Lattice Truss over a branch of the Little Warrior River.

Age is relative. Old Easley/Rosa Bridge is younger than I am and young in the world of covered bridges. This is a fun bridge to find. You will know you're nearly there when you come to Rosa Church. From Cleveland, go east on U.S. 231 to County Road 33 four miles west of Oneonta, then one and three-quarter miles right on County Road 33, and one-quarter mile left to the bridge.

Old Easley/Rosa Bridge is of modest size. The upper half of the sides are open and the Town Lattice Truss can be seen clearly. The roof projects out over the portals. We liked the appearance and size—a change from Swann/Joy. It captured our full attention and we were oblivious to a car full of local people who crossed the bridge until they gave us a rousing cheer when they saw our Washington State license plate.

37 *Highest Above the River*

Horton Mill Bridge (01-05-07), built in 1934, has two Town Lattice Truss spans, a total length of 220 feet and sits 70 feet above the Calvert Prong of the Little Warrior River. Located north of Oneonta, Alabama.

Horton Mill Bridge is also near Oneonta. We return east on U.S. 231 to Alabama 75 and drive north five miles. The bridge is on the left, and crosses the Calvert Prong of the Little Warrior River. This bridge is reputed to be higher above the river it crosses than any other covered bridge in the United States.

[Above] 35. Swan/Joy Bridge, Alabama, 1991

[At left] 36. Old Easley/Rosa Bridge, Alabama, 1991

The Horton Mill Bridge and its setting are described in *Alabama's Covered Bridges* by Tom and Dess Sangster. "Securely fastened on ledgerock and supported in the center by a towering concrete and masonry pier, the bridge majestically spans a rocky gorge—. Horton Mill is a breathtaking 70 feet above the riverbed, making it possibly the highest covered bridge above water in the nation. The nature trail takes you down the steep canyon slope, through a natural rock tunnel before leading you to the river bottom."

We arrived at the bridge on a rainy, drizzly morning, and could only partially experience the majestic setting of Horton Mill Bridge. The vivid description of the bridge by the Sangsters is the next best thing to seeing it in person.

Horton Mill Bridge is open to car traffic. It is

37. Horton Mill Bridge, Alabama, 1991

owned by the Alabama Historical Commission, and like a number of covered bridges in the United States, is on the National Register of Historic Places.

Bonus Bridge at Talladega

The Waldo/Riddle Mill Bridge (01-61-02) is a 115-foot long Howe and Queenpost Truss combination built about 1858 across Talladega Creek at Waldo, Alabama.

We head southeast on U.S. 231 to Interstate 20 and drive east toward Georgia. But first we have an opportunity to visit one of the older covered bridges in Alabama. We exit Interstate 20 to Alabama State Highway 77 and go south through the town of Talladega for four miles and turn left on a private road to Riddle Mill.

The Waldo/Riddle Mill Bridge is one that

Elizabeth and I missed in 1991 because of incredibly bad timing—being in the area during the Talladega auto races and desperately hunting for a motel.

One Hundred Thirty Years In and Out of the Rain

Concord/Ruff Mill/Nickajack Creek Bridge (10-33-02), southwest of Smyrna, Georgia, on Concord Road. Built in 1872 with a Queenpost Truss, two spans and a total length of 132 feet across Nickajack Creek.

The Concord/Ruff Mill/Nickajack Creek Bridge near Smyrna, Georgia is our next planned stop. It was a terrible rainy day in 1991, and we escaped from the Interstate 285 bypass at Smyrna, stopped for coffee, and tried to figure out what to do.

"This weather is impossible. We can't try to find a covered bridge in this downpour. Let's find a motel and look for the bridge tomorrow."

Fortified by the coffee, we returned to the car and began looking for a motel. Almost by accident we came to Concord Road. The covered bridge we were going to look for is on Concord Road, so I ignored the storm, drove on taking Concord Road south out of Smyrna, and found Concord/Ruff Mill/Nickajack Creek Bridge. Betty was a covered bridge fan, but not a covered bridge nut. She remained in the car while I stepped out into the downpour with two cameras. One shot with each camera was enough.

Concord/Ruff Mill/Nickajack Creek Bridge began life in 1872 as a way across a stream to a mill and a rural area. In those days, it was remote from Smyrna, Atlanta, and other urban places. Today the bridge finds itself on a busy, black-topped suburban road, part of the urban area. The bridge has been fulfilling its purpose, carrying traffic for one hundred thirty years, with the roof and siding protecting the structure on the one hundred and twenty days each year when it rains.

Stone Mountain Bridge

College Avenue/Stone Mountain/Effie's Bridge (10-44-01) was built in 1893 at Athens, Georgia, where College Avenue crossed the North Fork of the Oconee River. It was originally a 162 foot long Town Lattice Truss with two spans, but has been reduced to 151 feet.

Our tour heads east, through or around Atlanta to Athens, Georgia. Stone Mountain Park, just east of Atlanta, has many attractions: an antebellum mansion, relief statues of Jefferson Davis, Stonewall Jackson, and Robert E. Lee carved in the granitic mountain, and a covered bridge.

It's Sunny at Watson Mill

Watson Mill/Carlton Bridge (10-97-01), built about 1885, is a three-span Town Lattice Truss totaling 229 feet in length. It is located near Comer, Georgia, in Watson Mill Bridge State Park.

Watson Mill Bridge State Park is east of Athens. We exit Georgia State Highway 72 at Comer and go south on Georgia 22 to the park. In 1991, Elizabeth and I had an hour or so of pleasant weather and we fully enjoyed exploring the bridge and the park. [See the frontispiece of this book for an illustration of the bridge.]

The Watson Mill/Carlton Bridge sits low across the South Fork of Broad River just above a dam. The strong horizontal lines of the bridge and the dam combine to create an impressive

38. Concord/Ruff Mill/Nickajack Creek Bridge, Georgia, 1991

40. Campbell Bridge, South Carolina, 1991

Last Chance

effect. The park is well maintained with historic displays and information about the grist mill and saw mill that were once here. At times, picnics and square dances have been hosted at the bridge. Horace King, a freed slave, became a master builder of covered bridges in Georgia and Alabama. His son, Washington King, built the Watson Mill/Carlton Bridge.

We return north to Georgia State Highway 72 and continue east. The highway goes through Elberton, Georgia. Elberton has a town square with a Civil War statue and, around the square, stores and the Oglethorpe County Courthouse. We shopped in the stores years ago when our daughter, Mary, and her husband and children lived nearby at Dewy Rose. The town and the countryside enriched our experience of America.

Campbell Bridge (40-23-02), located near Gowensville, South Carolina, next to Pleasant Hill Road, has a 41-foot Howe Truss span of Beaver Dam Creek. It was built in 1909.

The next covered bridge on our tour is in South Carolina. Continuing east on Georgia State Highway 72 and South Carolina State Highway 72 and north on U.S. 25, we drive north through Greenville to South Carolina 414, then east to three-quarters of a mile west of the junction with South Carolina 14, and right one-quarter of a mile on Pleasant Hill Road. Campbell Bridge is just to the right on a section of the road that has been bypassed.

Campbell Bridge is the only remaining covered bridge in South Carolina. At first glance, it appears to be leaning in several directions. The

61

Looking Glass Falls, near Asheville, North Carolina, 1991

spent hours touring the Biltmore Mansion, the grounds, and gardens with many colors and varieties of flowers. I was impressed with the bowling alley on the lower level of the mansion.

Friends who live near Asheville showed us some of the lesser-known attractions of the area, including Looking Glass Falls. The next day Betty, Susan, and I drove across the Great Smoky Mountains, enjoyed the view from the tower near the summit, and continued to Gatlinburg, Tennessee, which also has many tourist attractions.

At Sevierville, it was time to stock up on groceries for our breakfast and lunch breaks. Elizabeth and Susan bought the food, and I followed behind carrying the bag of groceries. I impulsively stepped on a scale. A woman passing by looked twice at me, wondering perhaps if I knew my weight and wanted to know how much the groceries weighed, or if I knew how much the food weighed and was deducing my own weight, or if I knew nothing.

We enjoyed our diversions, but it was time to get back to covered bridges.

A View from the Bridge

Pigeon River Bridge (42-78-01), built in 1875, renovated in 1972. Spans the East Fork of Little Pigeon River with a 64-foot Queenpost Truss. Near Sevierville, Tennessee, at Harrisburg.

Driving east from Sevierville in Tennessee, we go three and three-quarter miles on U.S. 411, then right one-half mile on County Road 500, and one-quarter mile left on County Road 2712 to Pigeon River Bridge at the south edge of Harrisburg, Tennessee.

Pigeon River Bridge is small, weathered, in use, and provides access to a rural area outside of Harrisburg. The Queenpost Truss, consisting of diagonal wood beams separated by a horizontal wood beam, supports the 64-foot span. Simplic-

sides angle forward to support the roof as it extends out over the portals, and the buttresses on each side angle outward to brace the bridge against leaning sideways. Actually, the bridge is in good condition, standing erect, and painted red inside and out with white trim and a metal roof.

Interlude at Asheville

In April of 1991, Elizabeth and I, along with our daughter, Susan, headed for Tennessee. We had time to take an extra day at Asheville, North Carolina, an interlude from covered bridges. We

41. Pidgeon River Bridge, Tennessee, 1991. Below, an illustration of the Queenpost Truss on this bridge.

ity and usefulness are part of its charm. The openings on both sides below the horizontal beam provide light and air inside, and also provide framed views of the East Fork of Little Pigeon River. Pigeon Bridge is the oldest covered bridge remaining in Tennessee.

Elizabethton Bridge, in Town

The Elizabethton Bridge is probably the most impressive covered bridge remaining in Tennessee. In 1991, we missed this bridge, not realizing it could have been on our route. You can find it by returning to U.S. 411, and continuing east on 411 and U.S. 321 to Elizabethton.

I have seen pictures that show an attractive

structure with white horizontal siding and a green roof extending out over the portals, covering the roadway and an adjacent walkway. Two

63

small openings in the sides add to the distinctive appearance. The Doe River spills over a low dam just below the bridge.

The World Guide to Covered Bridges provides the following information. "Elizabethton Bridge (42-10-01), in Elizabethton on 3rd Street between Main Street and Riverside Drive. A 134 foot Howe Truss span of the Doe River, built in 1882."

An Engineer's Bridge

Bunker Hill Bridge (33-18-01), near Claremont, North Carolina, in a roadside park. Built in 1894 with an 85-foot Haupt Truss span over Lyle Creek. Renovated by Milton Graton Associates in 1994.

We continue east and south on U.S. 321 into North Carolina to Interstate 40 at Hickory, North Carolina, and east on I-40 a few miles to North Carolina State Highway 10, south to U.S. 64/70, west two and one-quarter miles to a roadside park. Bunker Hill Bridge is reached by a one-quarter mile walk on a trail in the park.

Bunker Hill Bridge is supported by the Haupt Truss. Herman Haupt was a railroad engineer. He is one of several bridge builders who accomplished minor miracles directing the replacement of railroad bridges destroyed during the Civil War. It is reported in the book *That Man Haupt* by James Arthur Ward that Abraham Lincoln, upon seeing one of Haupt's accomplishments, said: "That man Haupt has built a bridge across Potomac Creek, about 400 feet long and nearly 100 feet high, over which loaded trains are running every hour, and, upon my word, gentlemen, there is nothing in it but beanpoles and corn stalks."

42. Bunker Hill Bridge, North Carolina, 1991

43. Pisgah Bridge, North Carolina, 1991. Below are the stringers below the deck of the bridge.

With Susan leading the way, we soon reached the bridge. The bridge we saw was impressive if not spectacular. The unique truss design with diagonal beams crossing vertical beams forms a herringbone pattern. Dense foliage around the bridge made it difficult for us to get pictures, except head-on and inside, but the experience of walking through the park and seeing the bridge nestled into the greenery was well worth the while.

A Basic Bridge

Pisgah Bridge (33-76-01), near Pisgah, North Carolina, built about 1910. The 51 foot long stringer bridge has three spans across the Upper Branch of Little River.

Returning to Interstate 40, we continue east to U.S. 64 and southeast to U.S. 220, then south

to Ulah, North Carolina, west on County Road 1114 to Pisgah, and right two miles to Pisgah Bridge.

Pisgah Bridge is located on a piece of road that has been bypassed. This bridge was built without

65

Complete Coverage

a truss, and the support consists of horizontal wood beams, or stringers, below the bridge deck. The beams can support short spans and Pisgah Bridge has three spans for its 51-foot length, just 17 feet per span. It is unusual for this type of bridge to be covered because there is no truss above the deck that requires protection from inclement weather.

The bridge is attractively situated within a park. It has weathered, vertical siding, sits on rough stone piers, has triangular wood buttresses at each pier, and has a stained tin roof. We can more or less crawl under the bridge to see the heavy wood supporting beams below the deck.

Pisgah Bridge, washed out in a flash flood in August 2003 is scheduled to be restored in 2004.

Bob White Bridge (46-68-01), built in 1920, is 80 feet long with two Queenpost Truss spans of Smith River. It is located near Woolwine, Virginia.

We drive north on U.S. 220 into Virginia, go west on U.S. 58, and north on Virginia State Highway 8. Bob White Bridge is to the right about eight miles north of Stuart. If you miss the turnoff, return south from Woolwine for one and one-half miles and left one mile. The bridge is across Smith River on a section of Road 618 that has been bypassed.

Bob White Bridge, built in 1920, had deteriorated over the years, but had been rehabilitated when we saw it in 1991 and looked good. It has

44. Bob White Bridge, Virginia, 1991

45. Humpback Bridge, Virginia, 1991

two, 40-foot Queenpost Truss spans over the Smith River with a concrete pier supporting the bridge at its center. The bridge is sided inside and out, and the siding boards are vertical on the outside and diagonal on the inside.

Why the Hump?

Humpback Bridge (46-03-01), built near Covington, Virginia in 1857, with a 100 foot long arched Multiple Kingpost Truss span of Dunlap Creek.

Our next covered bridge is at Covington, Virginia. The Blue Ridge Parkway, a beautiful scenic drive with very little traffic, is our route part of the way between Woolwine and Covington. We continue north on Virginia 8 to reach the Parkway, go northeast to U.S. 60, and west on U.S. 60 and Interstate 64 to Covington.

Humpback Bridge, with a unique arched structure and set in a park, is a delight to see. We were there in April of 1991 when the trees had begun to flower. They added a dash of color in pleasant contrast to the dark, weathered siding of the bridge.

This open setting offers plenty of opportunities to view the bridge from the fronts, sides, and even from below. The portal entries are severe in appearance, but the gracefulness of the arched structure is apparent in the side view. We have the opportunity to look up from below at the timbers supporting the deck.

Why the hump? The rise at the center of the bridge adds to the strength of the truss. It is, in effect, a truss in the shape of an arch, combining the advantages of both structural types in one structure. Humpback Bridge, with its distinctive hump, is the last remaining covered bridge of this type built on the James River and Kanawha Turnpike.

46. Hern's Mill Bridge, West Virginia, 1991

A Peaceful Spot

Hern's Mill Bridge (48-13-01), a 54-foot Queenpost Truss span of Milligan Creek, built in 1884. Located near Lewisburg, West Virginia.

We are only a few miles from West Virginia and the next covered bridge on our tour. We return to Interstate 64, go west to the exit for U.S. 219 at Lewisburg, West Virginia, south to U.S. 60, west three and one-half miles, left one-quarter of a mile to Bunger's Mill Road, and left one mile on Hern's Mill Road.

Hern's Mill Bridge is just far enough out of Lewisburg to feel completely removed from the town. Here we find that all is quiet and peaceful. This little bridge fits into its setting. It has been here for over one hundred years, providing a needed crossing of Milligan Creek. Our red car

does not blend into the scene as well as the red bridge with its green roof.

The two covered bridges we've seen in West Virginia—Milton/Sinks Mill Bridge, part of the Middle America tour, and now Herns Mill Bridge—are on opposite sides of the state. In between is a lot of beautiful scenery, including the New River and the New River Gorge Bridge. It isn't far to these attractions and you might choose to include them in your tour route. However, our route heads northeast from Lewisburg to Frederick, Maryland.

In 1991, we had intended to include the New River Gorge and the New River Gorge Bridge (not covered) on our drive between Milton/Sink's Mill Bridge and Hern's Mill Bridge. Instead, because we were behind schedule due to the rain, in need of a motel room, bathroom, dinner, and sleep, we stayed on Interstate 64 to reach state 64 to reach Beckley. I rushed from the car to the motel office and my wet shoes went flying, taking me with them. I picked myself up, went into the motel office holding a handkerchief over my bleeding forehead, and asked for a room.

"You need to go to the hospital."

"We need a room."

Finally, after I produced Elizabeth and Susan, we got a room for three weary and desperate travelers, and Susan drove me to the hospital. I received three stitches with instructions to remove them after ten days. We didn't eat dinner out that night. Instead, Elizabeth and Susan made sandwiches and we ate in our room.

A couple of days later, when I went into a service station to pay for our gas, the cashier said, "You've been to the hospital."

"Yes. They opened up my head and put in some brains." Actually, my reply was just "Yes." The rest came to me a few days later. Meanwhile, Susan drove and I contemplated using my new brains.

Bonus Bridge: Philippi

Philippi Bridge (48-01-01) built in 1852 with two Burr Truss spans of the Tygart Valley River and a total length of 304 feet. The bridge is double-barreled with two traffic lanes and a pedestrian walkway. Located at Philippi, West Virginia.

If you drive northeast out of Lewisburg on U.S. 219 and north on U.S. 250/119, you will be able to see Philippi Bridge at the west edge of the town of Philippi. It is a most impressive structure, 304 feet long, supported by the Burr Truss, with two traffic lanes and an extra truss between the lanes.

Lemuel Chenoweth built Philippi Bridge and several others in West Virginia. I have read that he was taciturn and won contracts by building a scale model of a bridge, supporting it between

two chairs, and standing on it. He also bid low and built well.

Philippi Bridge was completed in 1852 and was situated on a turnpike. During the Civil War, the bridge was used by both North and South to move troops and supplies. In 1989, a fuel truck spill at the bridge ignited and Philippi Bridge was nearly destroyed. It was rebuilt in 1991, with steel beams added under the deck, and restored to its original appearance. Elizabeth and I were not able to include Philippi Bridge in our travels, but you may choose to do so.

Utica Mills Up, Roddy Down

Utica Mills Bridge (20-10-01) at the southeast edge of Lewistown, Maryland, crosses Fishing Creek with two spans and a 100-foot long Burr Truss. Built about 1850.

Elizabeth and I stayed overnight at Frederick, Maryland, in 1997, and had time to explore the city. The Barbara Fritchie House was open and we learned from the guide the story behind the partly legendary confrontation between Widow Fritchie and Southern troops as she stood at the curb defiantly waving the flag and saying, "Shoot if you must this old gray head, but spare the country's flag." A pleasant garden and a stream can be seen at the rear of the house. Barbara Fritchie House at Frederick would be an enjoyable place to live, but it would be inconvenient to have tourists continually passing through. The next day we drove north on U.S. 15 to Lewistown, Maryland. Utica Mills Bridge is one-quarter of a mile south of the main intersection in town, then left one mile.

Utica Mills Bridge was originally built about 1850 across the Monocacy River three miles east of its present location. A flood in 1889 carried it part way to Lewistown. The bridge was needed there, so half of the bridge was salvaged and rebuilt across Fishing Creek.

47. Utica Mills Bridge, Maryland, 1997

Barbara Fritchie House, Frederick, Maryland, 1997

The Utica Mills Bridge has been through other hard times. In 1993, an oversized truck damaged a structural beam. The bridge was restored by Arnold Graton and Associates (Arnold is a son of Milton Graton) and rededicated in May of 1997. We saw it that September, refreshingly new with red paint and a white cedar shingled roof. The bridge is generously wide.

Roddy Bridge (20-10-02), a 39-foot King-post Truss across Owens Creek at Thurmont, Maryland, built about 1850.

Nearby, north of Thurmont, is the location of Roddy Bridge. This bridge collapsed in 1997, and was gone when we looked for it that September. We hope it will be, or has been, restored.

48. Gilpin Bridge, Maryland, 1997

48 *Samuel Gilpin's Bridge*

Gilpin Bridge (20-07-01) built in 1860 near Bayview, Maryland. The 119-foot Burr Truss span crosses Northeast Creek.

Our route returns south to Frederick and east on Interstate 70 to Baltimore, east on Interstate 95 to exit 8 and north on Maryland State Highway 272 for one and one-quarter miles.

Gilpin Bridge is on a section of the highway that has been bypassed. It has a 119-foot Burr Truss span of Northeast Creek. The bridge was built in 1860 to provide access to Samuel Gilpin's flour mill. The Cecil County Historical Society and the State of Maryland restored the bridge in 1959.

Gilpin Bridge has horizontal siding, is painted red, and has narrow openings at eye level and below the eaves to admit light and ventilation.

The Burr Truss combines four arches with each truss, much like the Newport Bridge in Indiana. We notice that it has a bit of a sag, not too surprising for a bridge one hundred forty years of age.

49 *One of Three in Delaware*

Wooddale Bridge (08-02-04), near Hockessin, Delaware. A 60-foot Town Lattice Truss crossing Red Clay Creek. Built in 1870.

Wilmington, Delaware, is to the east. Returning to Interstate 95, we drive to Wilmington, exit to Delaware State Highway 48, go north to Rollingmill Road, and right one-quarter of a mile to Wooddale Bridge. If you reach Delaware

49. Wooddale Bridge, Delaware, 1997

41, you've gone too far. Return about three miles on Delaware 48. When you see a golf course on the right, Rollingmill Road is on the left.

We approached the bridge from the north and turned off too soon into a suburban residential area. At times like this it helps to get directions. A gentleman was working in his yard and he obliged us with some excellent information regarding directions to the golf course, which got us to where we belonged. I've passed on his directions, since he may not be in his yard to give them to you personally.

Wooddale is one of only three covered bridges in Delaware. We failed to find Ashland Bridge (08-02-02). We missed Smith Bridge No. 2 (08-02-01). The original 154 foot Burr Truss structure built in 1839 across Brandywine Creek near the north edge of the state was destroyed by arson in 1961. Finally the bridge has been replaced. The new bridge was dedicated on January 11, 2003.

Wooddale Bridge has a 60-foot Town Lattice Truss span of Red Clay Creek. It is a charming, small bridge in a wooded setting, with red vertical siding accented by white at the portals. The bridge, washed out in September 2003 by tropical storm "Henri", is scheduled to be to restored to again provide access to Foxhill Lane.

We have traveled about sixteen hundred miles from Cullman, Alabama. Our next covered bridge destination is at Lancaster, Pennsylvania. We can get there by continuing on Delaware 48 to Delaware 41 and Pennsylvania State Highway 41 and connecting with U.S. 30. But first we will spend some time in Philadelphia.

Chapter Five

THE MIDDLE ATLANTIC AND NEW ENGLAND

Interlude at Philadelphia

Early in 1997 I said, "We still haven't seen any covered bridges in Maryland, Delaware, New Jersey, New York, Connecticut, or Massachusetts." Elizabeth replied, "Let's see them." (And get it over with!) In September of 1997, we had already been to bridges in Maryland and Delaware and were ready to see and learn about Philadelphia and the historic events leading up to the establishment of the United States.

We began with a Gray Line tour of historic Philadelphia. The driver was a fountain of knowledge. He drove, stopped in busy streets oblivious to traffic, and told us all there was to know about what we were seeing. Our daughter, Susan, and her husband Greg joined us a few days later and together we revisited some of the tour sites and found other attractions. Armed with several pocketfuls of quarters for parking meters, we saw Carpenters Hall, where the first Continental Congress met in 1774, Constitution Hall, Independence Hall, Independence Square, the Betsy Ross House, Elfreth's Alley, and the Liberty Bell all in one compact area.

The Liberty Bell symbolizes the spirit of freedom, a mighty force in the 1770s that caused people to fight for and to achieve independence. As tourists, we appreciated the guides at the Liberty Bell who explained a great deal to a lot of people in a short time and still left us enough time to take a close look at the bell individually. Greg never misses an opportunity like that.

Liberty Bell, Philadelphia, 1997

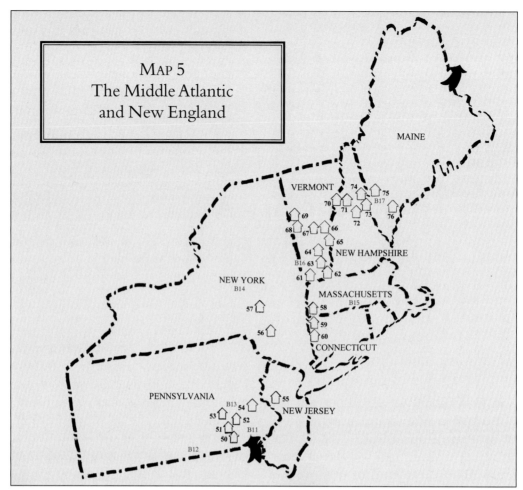

MAP 5
The Middle Atlantic
and New England

MAINE

VERMONT
74 75
70 71 B17
69 73 76
68 67 66 72
65
64
B16 63 NEW HAMPSHIRE
61 62

NEW YORK
B14
57
MASSACHUSETTS
B15
58
56 59
60
CONNECTICUT

PENNSYLVANIA
B13 54 55
53 52 NEW JERSEY
51 B11
50
B12

The Bridge at Valley Forge

Knox/Valley Forge Bridge (38-15-15), a 66-foot long Burr Truss built in 1865. Crosses Valley Creek at Valley Forge, Pennsylvania.

Valley Forge is west of Philadelphia on the way to Lancaster. The park is beautifully landscaped, which was almost a disappointment as we had expected to see a desolate land where George Washington and his troops had spent a miserable winter.

Knox/Valley Forge Bridge within the park looked familiar because we had seen it in photos friends had given to us. This covered bridge is 66 feet in length with white horizontal siding. The tops of the low arches can be seen in the open space at railing height. Built in 1865, this bridge replaced the original structure, which was built in 1851 and later destroyed in a flood.

The Bridge at Gettysburg

Saucks Bridge (38-01-01), built in 1854, supported by a 102-foot long Town Lattice Truss across Marsh Creek at Gettysburg, Pennsylvania, has red horizontal siding and open strips along the sides.

Covered bridges did not exist during the Revolutionary War, but some did play significant roles during the Civil War. The covered bridges at Valley Forge and Gettysburg can be an important part of your visit to these historic sites and they are included here as bonus bridges.

Saucks Bridge at Gettysburg, built in 1854, resounded to the feet of troops of General Robert E. Lee in a retreat in 1863 following their defeat in Pickett's Charge. Union forces also used the bridge, and it survived the battles around Gettysburg. Built in 1854, the bridge was washed out by a flood in 1996 and may have been reassembled by now.

50 *Herr Mill Village*

Herr Mill/Soudersburg Bridge (38-36-21), near Paradise, Pennsylvania. A two-span, 178-foot long Burr Truss across Pequea Creek, built in 1885.

Our tour continues west from Philadelphia on U.S. 30. Two miles east of Paradise in the Lancaster area, we turn left at Ronks Road and find Herr Mill/Soudersburg Bridge one-half mile down the road on the left. The bridge, a favorite with tourists, is now part of an Amish village.

Herr Mill/Soudersburg Bridge is a long, two-span crossing of Pequea Creek. It has dark-brownish siding with rectangular openings in the sides near each end and a small "eyebrow" roof over each opening. A trip through the bridge in a horse-drawn Amish buggy is included in the price of admission to the village. Brown doors at the portals keep the interior closed except to paying customers. The exterior can be seen and appreciated from a landscaped area along the river.

We stayed overnight at Lancaster in 1997,

allowing ourselves time to see some of the attractions of Amish country. We took a narrated bus tour of the rural area and visited a farm with the dairy barn and farmhouse full of Amish products for sale. There were souvenir shops, buggy rides, and a farm-style dinner where we shared a large table and got acquainted with other tourists. We began to understand why the Amish people cling to a simpler lifestyle and distance themselves from the temptation to display more wealth than their neighbors.

51 *Covered Bridge Shuffle* 52

Hunsecker Mill Bridge No. 2 (38-36-06), near Lancaster, Pennsylvania, originally built in 1843, replaced in 1975. Crosses the Conestoga River with a 181-foot Burr Truss span.

Pinetown Bridge (38-36-05), near Brownstown, Pennsylvania, built in 1867. Crosses the Conestoga River with a 135-foot Burr Truss span.

50. Herr Mill/Soudersburg Bridge, Pennsylvania, 1997

51. Hunsecker Mill Bridge No. 2, Pennsylvania, 1997

52. Pinetown Bridge, Pennsylvania, 1997

53. Rosehill/Wenger Bridge, Pennsylvania, 1997

Returning to U.S. 30, we continue west on U.S. 30 and the U.S. 30 bypass to Pennsylvania State Highway 272, north two and one-half miles, and right one and three-quarter miles on Hunsecker Road.

Hunsecker Mill Bridge was born to wander. In 1869, a flood lifted it off its abutments, carried the bridge down the Conestoga River and deposited it in a field. The bridge was dismantled and reconstructed on new abutments built three feet higher than the old ones.

Pinetown Bridge also crosses the Conestoga River. We continue north on Pennsylvania 272 to Creek Road one-half mile south of the intersection of 272 and Pennsylvania 722, and go right one quarter mile on Creek Road.

Pinetown Bridge was built in 1867, seventeen feet above the river. This was high enough until 1972. Tropical storm Agnes hit in 1972. Pinetown Bridge floated free at one end, swung around and pointed downstream, floated completely free, and headed for Hunsecker Mill

Bridge and disaster. Hunsecker Mill Bridge also floated off one abutment and swung sideways just in time for Pinetown Bridge to pass by. The two bridges did not touch. The Pinetown Bridge continued downstream and beached itself.

By this time Hunsecker Mill Bridge had floated completely free of its abutments and headed downstream past the beached Pinetown Bridge, finally crashing into a concrete bridge over Highway 23. Pinetown Bridge was dismantled by an Amish crew and rebuilt on its original abutments. Hunsecker Mill Bridge, damaged beyond repair, was rebuilt on its abutments in 1975 using all new materials.

We knew about the misadventures of these two bridges in advance and were anxious to see them. Each is supported by the Burr Truss with its familiar combination of truss and arch, and both have the raised approaches and stone abutments. Pinetown Bridge is red with white trim at the portals. Hunsecker Mill Bridge was not painted when we saw it in 1997.

53 *Hip Boots*

Rosehill/Wenger Bridge (38-36-14), near Brownstown, Pennsylvania, built in 1849. Crosses Cocalico Creek with an 89-foot Burr Truss.

Rosehill/Wenger Bridge is nearby. To find it, go back to Pennsylvania 272 for one mile south of its intersection with Pennsylvania 722, then right one-half mile on Rose Hill Road. You should be at the bridge.

When Rosehill/Wenger Bridge was built in 1849, it was called Zooks Mill Bridge. Henry Zook built it for $700 to provide access to his woolen mill. Times changed, the area became suburban, and the name of the bridge was changed to fit its new environment.

In 1972, tropical storm Agnes flooded Cocalico Creek and its watershed, and the water rose six feet above the deck of Rosehill/Wenger Bridge. The bridge stood firm. When we saw it in

1997, it was painted red with white trim. A marker six feet above the deck floor shows how high the water came in 1972. We were gawking and admiring the bridge when a carload of local people crossed the bridge and greeted us, much like the group back in Alabama at the Old Easley/Rosa Bridge.

B13 *Finding Wertz/Red Bridge*

Wertz/Red Bridge (38-06-06), near Reading, Pennsylvania, a single 218-foot Burr Truss span of Tulpehocken Creek, built in 1869.

Our tour route continues from Lancaster to Allentown, Pennsylvania. U.S. 222 passes just north of Reading and the Wertz/Red Bridge. You can find the bridge by exiting U.S. 222 to Pennsylvania State Highway 183, going southeast

B13. Wertz/Red Bridge, Pennsylvania, 2001

54. Bogert Bridge, Pennsylvania, 1997

54

*Big Bridge Over
Little Lehigh Creek*

**Bogert Bridge (38-39-01) built in 1841 with
a 169-foot Burr Truss span. Crosses Little
Lehigh Creek just south of Allentown,
Pennsylvania.**

a short distance to Van Reed Road, a short block
south to Red Bridge Road, and west a block to
the bridge. This sounds so easy I can't imagine
why we spent an hour being lost.

The first view of Wertz/Red Bridge is the
portal with its stepped "false front." The view
from the side reveals a shingled gable roof and
horizontal red siding. The single span across
Tulpehocken Creek also crosses the former
Union Canal.

The bridge, at 218 feet long, is the longest single span Burr Truss covered bridge in America.
Each truss has three arches, one on the outside
edge and two overlapping arches on the inside.
The arches and trusses are of Eastern white pine
secured together with oak pins.

The Berks County Heritage Center, near the
bridge, is a source of information about the history of agriculture, rural industry, and transportation in the area.

Approaching Allentown on U.S. 222, we go
southeast on Pennsylvania State Highway 309 to
Pennsylvania 29, south on 29 for a half mile, then
left one mile on Hatchery Road to Bogert Bridge.

Bogert Bridge is located in Little Lehigh Park.
It was built in 1841 with a 169-foot Burr Truss
crossing the Little Lehigh Creek. The green and
open park is interspersed with trees, and it provides an excellent setting for the red bridge with
its massive stone approaches and abutments. The
tops of the great arches of the Burr Truss can be
seen at the center of the open strip below the
eaves. Concrete piers have been added to limit
further sagging in the lengthy old bridge.

55. Green Sergeants Bridge, New Jersey, 1997

*Last Covered Bridge
in New Jersey*

**Green Sergeants Bridge (30-10-01), near
Sergeantsville, New Jersey. Built in 1866.
Crosses Wickeheoke Creek with an 84-foot
Queenpost Truss.**

Our route is southeast on Pennsylvania State
Highway 309 and east on U.S. 202 to cross the
Delaware River between New Hope, Pennsylvania, and Lambertville, New Jersey. Then we drive
left on New Jersey State Highway 29 to Stockton, right on County Road 20 to Sergeantsville,
then one and one-quarter miles left on the road
to Rosemont.

Green Sergeants Bridge is the last covered
bridge in New Jersey. It was scheduled for
removal, but a ground swell of protest saved the
bridge. The New Jersey State Highway Department disassembled, reinforced, and reassembled

the bridge. A special dedication ceremony was
held in 1961. The covered bridge carries traffic in
one direction, and an adjacent concrete bridge
carries traffic in the opposite direction.

About fifty covered bridges were built in New
Jersey over the years. Most impressive were the
ones that crossed the Delaware River between
New Jersey and Pennsylvania. The location of
our crossing between New Hope and Lambertville was, from 1813 to 1903, a covered
bridge 1,051 feet long with five spans.

While in New Jersey, we indulged in a bit of
nostalgia. With Greg's help, we located in Red
Bank, New Jersey, the address where Betty and I
lived briefly after our wedding in September of
1944. The rooming house was gone, but not our
memories of the two short months we spent
together before Betty returned to her hometown and I was shipped overseas.

80

56

Bypassed at Thruway Speed

Perrine Bridge (32-56-01). Built in 1844 with a 154-foot Burr Truss across the Wallkill River. Near Rifton, New York.

Returning to U.S. 202 from Sergeantsville and driving east, we reach Interstate 287, connect with I-87, and proceed rapidly north into New York State. Our destination is a covered bridge near Rifton, within sight of the Interstate. It is necessary to exit to New York State Highway 299 at New Paltz, go north on New York 32 to New York 213, and one-quarter mile east.

This is Perrine Bridge, built in 1844. Plans for a new freeway almost finished Perrine Bridge. It was in the way and scheduled for demolition, but the highway designers were persuaded to alter the path of the new freeway enough to save the bridge. Perrine Bridge deteriorated over the years and underwent extensive repairs in 1969. When we arrived in 1997, Perrine Bridge was again undergoing renovation. The bridge deck

was temporarily a workplace and timber, siding, and roofing repair was underway.

The bridge sits high above the scenic Wallkill River, an attractive setting with opportunities to view the bridge from the riverbank.

57

Longest of the Long

Blenheim Bridge (32-48-01), built in 1855 with a double-barreled Long Truss and Arch with a single 210-foot span of Schoharie Creek at North Blenheim, New York.

We can enjoy the scenery while driving to our next bridge at North Blenheim, New York. We go north on New York 213 to Kingston, west on New York 28, north on New York 30, through the Catskill Mountains to North Blenheim, and east on County Road 31 for one-quarter mile. Blenheim Bridge crosses Schoharie Creek at the east edge of town.

56. Perrine Bridge, New York, 1997

Nicholas Powers built Blenheim Bridge using a Long Truss and arch combination for a single 210-foot span across Schoharie Creek. The bridge was partially supported by scaffolding during construction. Clara C. Wagerman, in *Covered Bridges of New England,* relates that when the bridge was completed and just before the blocks between it and the scaffolding were knocked out, "Powers sat in the center of the bridge with his feet hanging downward and said

'If the bridge goes down, I never want to see the sun rise again,' but it settled only a fraction of an inch—less than he had allowed for."

Blenheim Bridge is a tribute to superior bridge design and workmanship. It is taller than most covered bridges to allow sufficient height for the massive arch extending from below the deck to the ceiling. This arch can be seen between the two traffic lanes of this double-barreled bridge. It is actually three arches, one above the other, with spaces in between. While the truss and arch are of wood, the wood structural members are joined by many pounds of nuts, bolts, and washers.

The bridge has natural, weathered vertical siding, an open strip below the eaves, and a tin roof. Blenheim Bridge was closed to vehicles in 1931. It is accessible from one end only, as the approach from the other end was washed out years ago by a flood.

B14

Oldest of the Old?

Hyde Hall Bridge (32-39-01), near East Springfield, New York, in Glimmerglass State Park. Built in 1825 with a 53-foot Burr Truss, it is across Shadow Brook in the park. The bridge has red horizontal lap siding.

Hyde Hall Bridge, which may be the oldest remaining covered bridge in America, is in Glimmerglass State Park, north and west of North Blenheim near U.S. 20 and East Springfield, New York. (Pulp Mill Bridge in Vermont is about the same age.) Hyde Hall is the name of an estate where the bridge was originally located. New York State now owns and maintains the bridge. Glimmerglass State Park and the Baseball Hall of Fame in nearby Cooperstown offer diversions from covered bridges.

57. Blenheim Bridge, New York, 1997

Double Barreled Blenheim Bridge with Long Truss and Arch

58   *The Bridge That Was and Is*

Upper Sheffield Bridge No. 2 (21-02-01), at Sheffield, Massachusetts, a 93-foot Town Lattice Truss span of the Housatonic River. Built in 1832, burned in 1994, replaced in 1998.

Continuing from North Blenheim to Albany, New York, and by Interstate 90 to U.S. 7 in Massachusetts, we go south to Sheffield, looking for the Upper Sheffield Bridge on Covered Bridge Lane at the north edge of town. In 1997, we missed the sign for the lane, and when we returned later we found that there was no sign. But it sure looked like a covered bridge lane. So we drove in one-quarter mile to the Housatonic River.

This is the site of Upper Sheffield Bridge, though the bridge is gone. The abutments are there, as is a large display with a description of the history of the bridge. The description ends with the words, "in the early morning of August 14, 1994, the venerable bridge was burned to the ground. Some materials salvaged from the earlier structure will be used for continuity in the reconstruction of this valued landmark."

Upper Sheffield Bridge, the oldest remaining covered bridge in Massachusetts, was built in 1832 with a 93-foot Town Lattice Truss. In 1981, it was restored, placed on raised concrete abutments, and rededicated. The loss in 1994 was especially tragic because of the work that had recently been done to restore it.

The bridge has been replaced, as promised, and can be seen at the end of Covered Bridge Lane. We saw and photographed it as a special part of our trip to New England in 2001. Upper Sheffield Bridge sits comfortably on its abutments. We hope that it will endure.

58. Abutments, Upper Sheffield Bridge site, Massachusetts, 1997

58. Upper Sheffield Bridge, Massachusetts, 2001

B15 *Vermont Bridge in Massachusetts*

Vermont Bridge (21-14-03) is a 55 foot long Town Lattice Truss built about 1870. Located across Quinebaug River Arm.

Although we did not include it in this tour, the opportunity exists to visit Old Sturbridge Village in Massachusetts. Vermont Bridge, originally located near West Dummerston, Vermont, has been relocated in the village.

We had intended to stop in 1997, but we arrived too late in the day and the center was closed. Old Sturbridge Village is a collection of old buildings moved from various locations in New England to recreate a rural village with costumed "residents" reenacting daily life as it was in the 1870s. The village has shops, grist mills and saw mills, and gardens. Though we missed seeing the village, we saw a similar restored village in New Brunswick, Canada, in 1986.

59 *Real Windows*

West Cornwall/Hart Bridge (07-03-02) built in 1841 at West Cornwall, Connecticut, with two spans, a Town Lattice and Queenpost Truss combination, and a length of 242 feet across the Housatonic River.

Continuing south on U.S. 7 to West Cornwall, Connecticut, we find the West Cornwall/Hart Bridge in town on Connecticut State Highway 128 just east of U.S. 7. The Housatonic River is wide here and two spans and a total length of 242 feet are required to cross it. In September of 1997, we had the opportunity to view the bridge from different angles, including from the riverbed because the water was low.

The river has had its moments at West Cornwall and took out an earlier bridge in 1837. An ice jam was dynamited in 1964 to save the present bridge. The bridge has been raised two feet and a steel deck has been added, hidden inside

59. West Cornwall/Hart Bridge, Connecticut, 1997

the existing structure. It has a shake roof, red siding, and real windows with glass instead of the usual openings. The rehabilitated bridge was reopened in 1973.

60 George Washington Crossed Here

Bull Bridge (07-03-01), near Kent, Connecticut. Built in 1842 with a single 109-foot span of the Housatonic River using a combined Town Lattice Truss and Queenpost Truss.

We continue south on U.S. 7 to the village of Bull Bridge south of Kent. The bridge is one-quarter mile to the right on Bull Bridge Road.

The bridges at Bull Bridge go back to 1760 when Isaac Bull and his son Jacob built a low bridge across the Housatonic River to provide access to their mill and iron works. At least four bridges were lost to floods. The present bridge is placed high above the turbulent waters at this narrow channel of the river.

One of those early bridges, begun about 1782, was partly completed when George Washington crossed on his way from Litchfield, Connecticut to Morehouse Tavern in Wingdale, New York. The story, as told by Andrew R. Howard in his book *Covered Bridges of Connecticut,* is that "Jacob Bull laid planks down and led General Washington's horse across, while the General followed on foot. Obviously at this time it was an uncovered span, and it is not certain when it became covered." Howard concludes that it must have been covered before Jacob Bull's death in 1811.

The present Bull Bridge was built in 1842 and is plain in appearance, with vertical gray siding broken only by tiny, spaced openings. The length of the vertical siding has been increased to cover steel beams added below the deck in 1969.

The river was low in September of 1997, with the riverbed boulders exposed, and our "children," Sue and Greg, delighted in scrambling around on the boulders and in helping us find interesting places to view the bridge.

60. Bull Bridge, Connecticut, 1997

61. Henry Bridge, Vermont, 2001

The Village Blacksmith

Henry Bridge (45-02-02) built about 1840, 121 feet in length, spans the Walloomsac River at North Bennington, Vermont.

Driving back north on U.S. 7 to Bennington, Vermont, we find our next covered bridge. Henry Bridge, at North Bennington, crosses the Walloomsac River with a 121-foot Town Lattice Truss. The structure was adequate for the normal horse-and-buggy and wagon traffic, but hauling pig iron from iron mines in the vicinity of Bennington introduced a special problem. Herbert Wheaton Congdon, in *The Covered Bridge,* describes the problem as "heavy loads of pig-iron, creaking ponderously along on huge wagons each drawn by several yokes of oxen."

The solution to the problem was to add an extra pair of trusses alongside the original ones. These matched pairs display strength, like the brawny arms of the Village Blacksmith in Longfellow's poem. We saw the bridge in 1986 with its matched pairs of trusses. The bridge has since been rebuilt and now has the single trusses seen in our 2001 photograph.

Silk/Locust Grove/Robinson Bridge (45-02-04) is like Henry Bridge, but is shorter at 88 feet. Both are off Vermont State Highway 67A, the Silk/Locust Grove/Robinson Bridge on Silk Road opposite Bennington College and the Henry Bridge about a mile before 67A joins Vermont 67.

Papermill Village

Papermill Village Bridge No.2 (45-02-03), at North Bennington, Vermont. Built in 1889 with a 131-foot Town Lattice Truss span of the Walloomsac River. Rebuilt in 2000.

B16. Papermill Village Bridge No. 2, Vermont, 2001

Papermill Village Bridge is between the Silk/Locust Grove/Robinson and Henry Bridges, about one-half mile past Silk Bridge and just to the left. Built in 1889, the bridge developed structural problems and was closed in 1986. Traffic was diverted to the temporary Bailey Bridge alongside. Finally, the cost and structural problems were solved, and Papermill Village Bridge was in use again in 2000.

Before 1800, one of the first paper mills in Vermont was located here. The site for the Papermill Village Bridge is most impressive. It has a 131-foot span of the Walloomsac River just above a dam. The Town Lattice Truss is visible in the wide, open strip between the red horizontal siding and the eaves.

Creamery Bridge

Creamery/Centerville Bridge (45-13-01), Brattleboro, Vermont. An 80-foot Town Lattice Truss span over Whetstone River, built in 1879.

Our route goes east on Vermont 9 to Brattleboro, Vermont. Creamery/Centerville Bridge is one-half mile west of Interstate 91 at Guilford Street. This bridge can be seen from Vermont 9. It is an easy place to stop, and we take a break from driving and riding.

The Brattleboro Creamery was once located in this area. The bridge was built in 1879 to replace one lost in a freshet the year before. It crosses Whetstone River with an 80-foot Town Lattice Truss. Creamery Bridge has a green slate roof, vertical red siding, white trim at the portals, and a pedestrian walkway.

62. Creamery/Centerville Bridge, Vermont, 1997

63   *Diamond-Studded*

West Dummerston Bridge (45-13-02), at West Dummerston, Vermont. Built in 1872. A Town Lattice Truss with two spans and a total length of 280 feet across the West River.

We head north out of Brattleboro on Vermont 30 to West Dummerston and turn right on East West Road. The West Dummerston Bridge is a magnificent structure spanning the West River. We visited here in 1986. The long bridge has a distinctive design and, with the mountains in the background, is most impressive.

One unique feature of the bridge is the diamond-shaped openings spaced at intervals to fit between the crossing diagonals of the Town Lattice Truss. The long rectangular openings near the ends provide needed daylight at the portals for drivers of vehicles moving from bright daylight into the semi-darkness of the bridge interior.

We are rewarded when, in pursuit of covered bridges, we find the unexpected. Newfane, Vermont, a few miles further north, is a fascinating town with several interesting buildings, including the Court House, the First Congregational Church, and the Union Hall, all painted white with black trim.

64   *Great Scott*

Scott Bridge (45-13-13), with three spans and a total length of 276 feet across the West River at Townshend, Vermont. The longest span, a Town Lattice Truss, was built in 1870. The two Kingpost Truss spans were added later.

We continue our pleasant drive north on Vermont 30 to Townshend. Here we find Scott Bridge, a long, three-span structure across the

63. West Dummerston Bridge, Vermont, 1986.

[At left] The Town Lattice Truss, West Dummerston Bridge.

West River. The original bridge was 166 feet long, supported by a Town Lattice Truss. Arches were added when the truss began to sag, but the addition of the arches was only partially success-ful because one arch collapsed. A concrete pier was then built under the center of the span.

The West River, during a freshet, washed out part of the west riverbank. Scott Bridge was caught short and had to be made longer by adding two more spans. The bridge is now 276 feet in length. The compensation for all this trouble is that Scott Bridge is now one of the longest covered bridges located entirely within the state of Vermont. (Cornish–Windsor Bridge, shared by New Hampshire and Vermont, is longer.) The bridge has vertical siding, a green tin roof, a collapsed arch, and a will to survive.

Newfance, Vermont, 1986

64. Scott Bridge, Vermont, 1986

65   *Cornish, New Hampshire— Windsor, Vermont*

Cornish-Windsor Bridge (29-10-09) crosses the Connecticut River between Cornish, New Hampshire, and Windsor, Vermont. Built in 1866, a 449-foot Town Lattice Truss with two spans.

We continue northerly on state highways to Windsor, Vermont. The Cornish-Windsor Bridge crosses the Connecticut River between Windsor and Cornish, New Hampshire. It is 449 feet in length, the longest covered bridge in the United States. It is the fourth bridge to cross the river here. The first, built in 1796, was not covered; the second, built in 1825, had covered trusses but no roof; the third, built in 1850, was roofed. The present bridge was built in 1866 after an ice jam carried away bridge number three.

When Elizabeth and I saw Cornish-Windsor Bridge in 1986, we noticed sags in the middle of the two Town Lattice Truss spans, but we drove across in comfort. The sag was measured at 18 inches in 1987, and renovation was underway in 1988. Repairs included new larger lower beams, new deck supports, a new deck, and repair to the trusses. The bridge was rededicated in 1989.

When we revisited Cornish-Windsor Bridge in 1997, we found it looked much as it had in 1986, except that the bridge now rose 18 inches to the center of each span. Susan and Greg saw it for the first time in 1997. Mary's first visit was in 2001.

This long bridge has two traffic lanes so it is not necessary to wait to cross. It is fairly busy and very popular. We end up on the New Hampshire side every time we visit, and we park and take photographs.

65. Cornish-Windsor Bridge, New Hampshire/Vermont, 1986

66 67 *Across the Ottauquechee*

Taftsville Bridge (45-14-12), at Taftsville, Vermont, built in 1836. Two Multiple Kingpost Truss and Arch spans of the Ottauquechee River with a total length of 189 feet. The arches extend below the bridge and anchor into the pier and the abutments.

We continue north in Vermont to White River Junction and west from there on U.S. 4 to Taftsville, go one-half mile past the junction with Vermont 12, then right to the Taftsville Bridge on River Road.

The Taftsville Bridge is long, with two spans totaling 189 feet crossing the Ottauquechee River. The bridge has red vertical siding with an open strip running the entire length and a tin roof. We saw the bridge in 1986. We returned for another visit in 2001, and we spent more time seeing it in its spectacular setting and scrambling down to the river's edge so that our photographs would include the bridge, the river, and dam.

Lincoln Bridge (45-14-13) built in 1877 near West Woodstock, Vermont. A 136-foot Pratt Truss and Arch across the Ottauquechee River.

Continuing west on U.S. 4 through Woodstock and three miles past the junction with Vermont 106 takes us to Lincoln Bridge on the left side of the highway on Fletcher Hill Road.

Lincoln Bridge has an unusual truss with a wooden arch as the top member and vertical beams and crossed diagonal iron rods between the arch and the wooden lower chord. The bridge has vertical, weathered natural siding and a steep-pitched, gable roof. The bridge has a single 136-foot span of the Ottauquechee River and was built in 1877.

65. Cornish-Windsor Bridge, New Hampshire/Vermont, 2001

66. Taftsville Bridge, Vermont, 2001

67. Lincoln Bridge, Vermont, 2001

Since we saw it in 1986, Lincoln Bridge has had a bright green metal roof with green skylights added. Considerable controversy resulted because those additions were a significant departure from the historic bridge appearance. Our 2001 photo shows the skylights, which were not present in 1986.

68 *No Lonesome Whistle*

East Shoreham Railroad/Rutland Railroad Bridge (45-01-05), near Shoreham Center, Vermont. A 109-foot Howe Truss span of the Lemon Fair River, built in 1897.

We continue west on U.S. 4 to Vermont Sstate Highway 30 and north on 30 for two and three-quarter miles past where Vermont 73 joins it from the east, then west on Shoreham-Whiting Road for two and three-quarter miles, and left three-quarters of a mile on East Shoreham Road. We have found an abandoned railroad and a covered railroad bridge.

The Addison Branch Railroad ran here until 1951, with trains crossing the Lemon Fair River on the East Shoreham Railroad/Rutland Railroad Bridge. The sound of approaching trains has been missing for many years, but the bridge remains, tall and narrow, and sturdy enough to support the engines and trains of those days.

It is peaceful at East Shoreham Railroad Bridge. We have the place to ourselves, with no cars, trains, or people except us. The tall bridge is stately, with weathered natural siding, and is well preserved.

69 *Senior Citizen*

Pulp Mill/Paper Mill Bridge (45-01-04) at Middlebury, Vermont. Built about 1820 as a single span double-barreled Burr Truss bridge 199 feet long across Otter Creek.

68. East Shoreham Railroad/Rutland Railroad Bridge, Vermont, 1986

Returning to Vermont 30, we continue north into Middlebury, find Vermont 23, and go northwest three-quarters of a mile past the intersection with Vermont 125 to Horse Road and Pulp Mill Bridge Road. Highways arrive at the center of Middlebury from all directions. The bridge should be easy to find, since it crosses Otter Creek in town, but we got lost in 1986 and saw quite a lot of Middlebury and its surroundings while looking for the bridge.

Pulp Mill/Paper Mill Bridge is possibly the

69. Pulp Mill/Paper Mill Bridge, Vermont, 2001

oldest covered bridge remaining in America and was built about 1820. Hyde Hall Bridge in New York was built in 1825. In any event, Pulp Mill/Paper Mill Bridge is old and well worth seeing. The original 199-foot single span developed a noticeable sag, so piers were added to reinforce it. Pulp Mill/Paper Mill Bridge, one of the double-barreled covered bridges once common on toll roads, has two narrow, but drivable, traffic lanes and still carries considerable traffic. Pedestrians have a separate, uncovered crossing.

 Two Baths in One Day

Bath-Haverhill/Woodsville Bridge (29-05-04), at Woodsville, New Hampshire. Built in 1829 with two spans, a 256-foot length supported by a Town Lattice Truss and Arch crossing of the Ammonoosuc River.

Our "Baths" are in New Hampshire. To get there, we first go north on U.S. 7 to Burlington, Vermont, where Elizabeth and I stayed overnight in 1986, then southeast to Montpelier, Vermont, where we visited the State Capitol grounds. Our route continues east on U.S. 302 to Woodsville, New Hampshire.

Bath-Haverhill/Woodsville Bridge is one-quarter mile north of U.S. 302 on New Hampshire State Highway 135. The bridge is impressive in many ways. Built in 1829, it is still in use. The bridge crosses the Ammonoosuc River in town where the river is dammed, creating a falls below the bridge.

The two-span, 256-foot long Town Lattice Truss and arch structure supports the wide, two-lane roadway. The roof extends out over a pedestrian walkway along one side. The bridge has red vertical siding with white trim at the portals. It was a challenge to photograph because of overhead wires and limited access to suitable places for viewing the bridge.

Bath Bridge (29-05-03) at Bath, New Hampshire, across the Ammonoosuc River. Built in 1832. Four spans and a total length of 375 feet.

70. Bath–Haverhill/Woodsville Bridge, New Hampshire, 1997

71. Bath Bridge, New Hampshire, 1997

Covered Bridge Campground

The town of Bath is a few miles east of Woodsville on U.S. 302. The Bath Bridge is located on Woodsville Road in town. Bath Bridge is an imposing structure, with four spans and a total length of 375 feet. It occupies a commanding location where it crosses the Ammonoosuc River with a dam and falls and a rugged riverbed below the bridge. Bath Bridge was raised and altered structurally with the addition of a new set of arches when the B&M Railroad was extended along the river. The high and low arches of the truss and diagonal beams are combined into a unique structure that defies classifying.

Elizabeth and I saw Bath Bridge in 1986, and again in 1997 with Sue and Greg. The trees had some color on that late September day in 1997, and with the town and church in the background, we enjoyed good photo opportunities.

Albany Bridge (29-02-06) built in 1858 four miles west of Conway, New Hampshire, on New Hampshire 112 at Covered Bridge Campground. A 120-foot Paddleford Truss and Arch span of the Swift River.

We have many favorite covered bridges among the one hundred we have included on this tour. Albany Bridge is, for us, a favorite among favorites. It is in a charming location where it crosses the Swift River and provides access to a campground.

In 1997, we visited Albany Bridge for the second time. (The first was in August of 1986.) It was late September and spectacular fall colors were beginning to appear. The colors added to the charm of the weathered gray bridge, its red roof, the cut stone abutments, and the rocky waters of the Swift River.

72. Albany Bridge, New Hampshire, 1997

73 74 *Two Bridges at Conway*

Saco River Bridge (29-02-03), in Conway, New Hampshire, built in 1890, has a Paddleford Truss with Arch, two spans and a total length of 225 feet across the Saco River.

The Albany Bridge and the two covered bridges we see in Conway are supported by the Paddleford Truss, which is found only in New England. The diagonals of this truss overlap near the bridge deck, a variation from other, similar, truss designs.

We take New Hampshire 112 east from Albany Bridge to New Hampshire 16 and Conway. The Saco River Bridge is in town on the old Highway 16 route at West Side Road. Swift River Bridge is on the nearby West Side Road on a section that has been bypassed.

The Saco River Bridge is a practical structure with two lanes for vehicular traffic and two pedestrian lanes all under one roof. The sides are open, making its use for cars and people comfortable and cheerful. We can see the Paddleford Truss and arch structure. The bridge in 1986 was white and weathered. In 1997, we found it had been repainted gray with white trim and a red roof.

Swift River Bridge (29-02-05) at Conway, New Hampshire. Built in 1870 with a 129-foot Paddleford Truss and Arch span across Swift River.

The Swift River Bridge is closed to traffic, but is maintained. It has red vertical siding and a green tin roof, and the bridge name and year built are on a plaque above the portal entry. The bridge sits on stone abutments, and we have a good opportunity to view the long Saco River Bridge from it.

73. Saco River Bridge, New Hampshire, 1997

74. Swift River Bridge, New Hampshire, 1986

 A Taste For Hemlock

Hemlock Bridge (19-09-02), near Fryeburg, Maine, crosses an old channel of the Saco River with a 116-foot Paddleford Truss and Arch. Built in 1857.

We head east from Conway on U.S. 302 into Maine for six miles east of the junction with Maine State Highway 5, then left on Hemlock Bridge Road for three serene miles of driving through the woods as the road reaches and crosses the Saco River on the Hemlock Bridge.

We arrived at Hemlock Bridge in 1986 and were enthralled with the bridge, the river, and the greenery. This is actually the old channel of the Saco River, with quiet waters to match the quiet setting. While we were admiring the scene, a couple arrived by truck, launched a canoe, and paddled off into the stillness. The whole experi-

ence made a deep impression on us. The appearance of the bridge with its weathered vertical siding and small rectangular openings is enhanced by the beautiful setting. Hemlock Bridge, for Betty and me, is also a favorite among favorites.

 Porter/Parsonfield

Porter/Parsonfield Bridge (19-09-05) a 160-foot long Paddleford Truss and Arch crossing of the Ossippee River with two spans, built in 1858 between Porter and Parsonfield, Maine. In use until 1970.

The Ossippee River is the boundary between Oxford and York Counties in Maine. The towns of Porter in Oxford County and Parsonfield in

75. Hemlock Bridge, Maine, 1986

York County shared in the costs of construction and maintenance of the Porter/ Parsonfield Bridge. After a new, parallel concrete bridge was built, money to maintain the old covered bridge was hard to come by. When Betty and I stopped in 1986, we could see it was suffering from neglect. Recent major repairs have been made, and today the Porter/ Parsonfield Bridge is a valued local landmark.

To find the bridge, go south from Hemlock Bridge on Maine State highways 113 and 160. It is adjacent to 160 just south of Maine 25.

76

Worth Repeating

Babb's Bridge No. 2 (19-03-01), near South Windham, Maine. Built in 1976 with a 79-foot Queenpost Truss span of the Presumpscot River.

Returning from Hemlock Bridge to U.S. 302, we continue southeast on 302 and south on U.S. 202 about four miles to River Road, one mile north of the junction of Maine 237 and U.S. 202. We go west on River Road for one and one-half miles and then right one-half mile on Hurricane Road. Babb's Bridge can also be reached from Porter/Parsonfield Bridge by driving east on Maine 25 to U.S. 202, and then north.

Babb's Bridge, built in 1864, was destroyed by fire in 1973. It was replaced using new materials, duplicating the design of the old bridge. Maine contributed $75,000 toward the cost. The new Babb's Bridge was dedicated in 1976. When we saw it in 1986, the bridge still had that new look. It has rounded portal entries, vertical siding, and cut stone abutments. The bridge is supported by a 79-foot long Queenpost Truss span of the Presumpscot River.

76. Babb's Bridge No. 2, Maine, 1986

Interlude in Maine

We had an enjoyable time in Portland, Maine, in 1986, which included a walking tour, visiting the lighthouse, and a boat ride on Casco Bay. The boat stopped at several islands, taking on and dropping off residents and freight. The residents and the tourists shared space on the boat, and we witnessed how the islanders commute. The day was pleasant and the walk enjoyable as we began at the waterfront, walked past the U.S. Customs House, City Hall, the Museum of Art, the commercial area, and returned to the waterfront.

Traveling north on Interstate 95, we stop for awhile at the Maine State Capital at Augusta. We have travelled about fifteen hundred miles from Philadelphia, Pennsylvania, which was the beginning of our tour through the Middle Atlantic and New England states to Houlton, Maine before we enter Canada.

Casco Bay, Maine, 1986

Chapter Six

EASTERN CANADA AND THE GREAT LAKES STATES

77 *A Quarter Mile Long and a Quarter Mile Wide*

Hartland Bridge (55-02-07), at Hartland, New Brunswick, built in 1921. Howe Truss with seven spans and a total length of 1,282 feet across the St. John River.

U.S. Interstate 95 ends at the Canadian border between Houlton, Maine, and Woodstock, New Brunswick. We continues east on New Brunswick Provincial Highway 95 to Woodstock and north on Trans-Canada Highway 2 to Hartland.

Hartland Bridge is secure in its title of "the longest covered bridge in the world" and has no close competitors. The first bridge here was built in 1898–99 as a private toll bridge. The seven uncovered spans sat on wood crib piers filled with rock. New Brunswick Province acquired the bridge in 1907, eliminated the toll, and rebuilt the bridge in 1921 with covered Howe Truss spans set on massive, new concrete piers.

It is difficult to grasp Hartland Bridge's great length of 1,282 feet. When seen from either end, the seven spans are compressed into a foreshortened view. Seen from the new bridge upstream, the bridge stretches into a long, thin line. The seven spans are the equivalent of seven bridges end to end. The bridge is sixteen feet wide inside, wide enough for cars to pass. There is a pedestrian walkway along the downstream side. Hartland Bridge is open to cars, but most traffic, including larger vehicles, uses the newer bridge.

Interlude in New Brunswick

We made three special stops in this part of New Brunswick in 1986. The first was Kings Landing, which is southeast of Hartland on Trans-Canada Highway 2. We found the pioneer village restored, with costumed employees spending their working hours living as the original inhabitants had. A wood crib dam produced water power to run a grain mill and a saw mill. Farm wagons circled around the buildings and croplands, and weary tourists could hitch a ride. In one house, women prepared stew from meat and vegetables produced at Kings Landing. I still think about how delicious that stew smelled.

We stayed overnight at Fredericton, the capital of New Brunswick, enjoyed a walking tour around town, and bought a souvenir plate of Hartland Bridge. On another day, at St. John, we saw the reversing falls where the river changes direction with the tides, and we explored the Market Square area of shops.

78 *Moose Call*

Moosehorn Bridge (55-06-29), near Norton, New Brunswick, built in 1915. Crosses Moosehorn Brook with a 98-foot Howe Truss.

Our route goes northeast from St. John on Provincial Highway 1. As we pass Bloomfield on

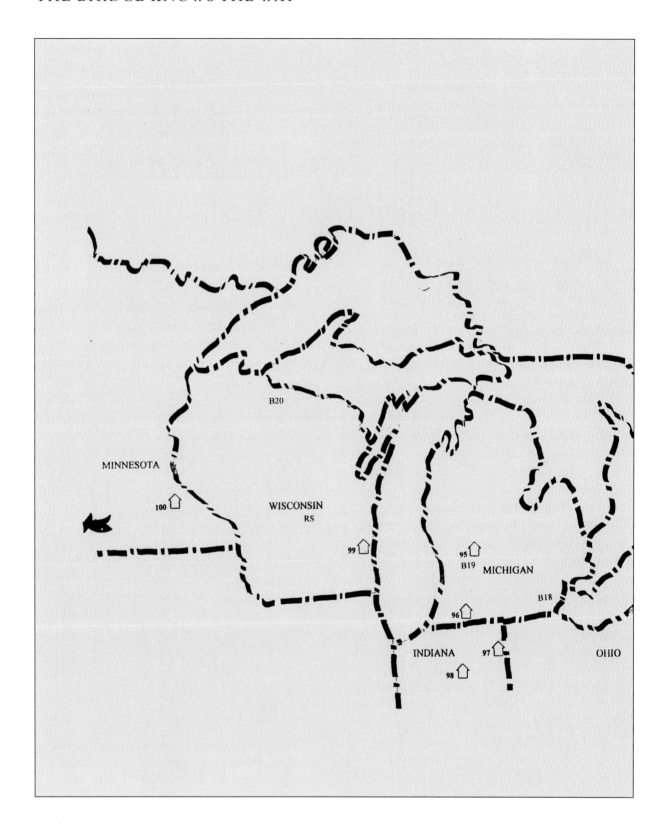

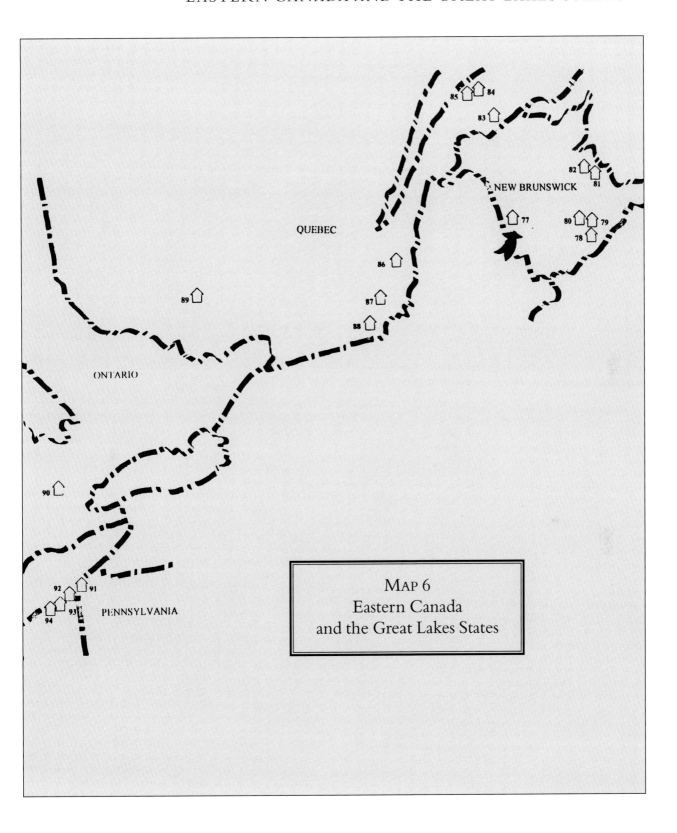

MAP 6
Eastern Canada
and the Great Lakes States

77. Hartland Bridge, New Bruswick, 1986. Below is a side view showing the seven spans.

the way to Norton, we see Moosehorn Bridge on our right. The bridge, built in 1915, has been bypassed, but is maintained. The bridge has vertical wood siding with diagonal wood inside at the entries. Care has been taken to replace missing siding with weathered boards from old barns to match the weathered original siding. We are free to look around with no cars to distract us, but we feel small when framed by this large, high structure.

79 A Useful Life

MacFarlane/Wards Creek No. 2 Bridge (55-06-13), near Sussex, New Brunswick. Built in 1909 with a 63-foot Howe Truss span of Wards Creek.

Continuing on Provincial Highway 1 to New Brunswick Highway 111 at Sussex, we go south four and one-half miles and right one mile on Wards Creek Road. On this occasion, we were four miles or so beyond Sussex, and should

Kings Landing, New Brunswick

78. Moosehorn Bridge, New Brunswick, 1986

79. MacFarlane/Ward's Creek No. 2 Bridge, New Brunswick, 1986.

already be at the bridge, but still had not found it. Still, I felt we were in the right area. We began going downhill, as if toward a creek. Wards Creek Bridge suddenly appeared. Betty said, "I think you smell those bridges."

Wards Creek Bridge is one of the small, still-in-use covered bridges in New Brunswick. It has a 63-foot Howe Truss, vertical, weathered wood siding, and generous width and height. The bridge and the road tempted us to continue to find out where the road would go, and the bridge knows the way, but we had other bridges to find, and so we returned to Sussex.

80 *Kennebecasis River Salmon*

Salmon/Kennebecasis River No. 8 Bridge (55-06-21), near Sussex, New Brunswick, built in 1907. A 119-foot Howe Truss span crosses the Kennebecasis River.

We return north to Trans-Canada Highway 2 and continue north of Sussex for three-quarters

of a mile on Provincial Highway 890. The Salmon/Kennebecasis River No. 8 Bridge crosses the Kennebecasis River in a roadside park at this location.

Salmon Bridge is typical of many of the covered bridges in New Brunswick—unpainted, weathered by the elements, maintained, with a tall profile and a steep roof. While most New Brunswick covered bridges continue to carry traffic, Salmon Bridge has been closed to vehicles, and a picnic table is placed inside the bridge for picnickers who prefer the shade or a dry spot on a rainy day.

81 *A Visit to St. Nicholas*

St. Nicholas River No. 1 Bridge (55-05-08), near Rexton, New Brunswick. Howe Truss with three spans and 504-foot length across the St. Nicholas River. Built in 1919, burned in 2001.

Trans-Canada Highway 2 takes us northeast to

80. Salmon/Kennebecasis River No. 8 Bridge, New Brunswick, 1986

81. St. Nicholas River No. 1 Bridge, New Brunswick, 1986

Moncton. In 1986, we stayed in Moncton for several days and took side trips to Prince Edward Island and Halifax, Nova Scotia. At Moncton, we watched the tidal bore come in from the Bay of Funday. It is a wave that moves inland, a visual sign of low tide changing to high tide.

We continue north on Provincial Highways 15 and 11 to Rexton. The place mats at our lunch stop show the location of several covered bridges in the area. Fortified with lunch and equipped with a place mat, we explore to the west of Rexton and find two covered bridges. First, out of Rexton on Highway 495 for about four and one-quarter miles, and right one-half mile on Highway 470, is the St. Nicholas River Bridge.

St. Nicholas River No. 1 Bridge crosses the river on Highway 470. It is 504 feet long, consisting of three spans with extra steel supports added. Some of the weathered vertical siding is missing. Gaps in the siding help to light the inside of the bridge, and we can clearly see the Howe Truss structure.

The bridge was destroyed by fire on February 26, 2001.

82 Tom Graham's Bridge

Tom Graham Bridge (55-05-03), near Rexton, New Brunswick, built in 1910. A 109-foot Howe Truss span of Tom Graham Creek.

The Tom Graham Bridge is nearby on Main River Road, two miles off Highway 470. It is a 109-foot span across Tom Graham Creek. We see it as typical of New Brunswick covered bridges —weathered, still in use, and attractive in its setting, with the water, the trees, and the road providing the perfect elements for photographic composition. The bridge approaches are on fill, and the creek is wider than the bridge is long. The road continuing on the other side of the bridge looks inviting, but we retrace our route to Rexton and proceed north.

83 Longest on the Matapédia

Routhierville Bridge (61-43-04), at Routhierville, Québec. Built in 1931 with two spans and 258-foot Town Lattice Truss across the Matapédia River.

Our tour continues north on New Brunswick Provincial Highways 11 and 8 to Campbellton, New Brunswick, and into Québec following Quebec Provincial Highway 132 as we continue west and north along the Matapédia River.

The first Québec covered bridge on the tour, Routhierville Bridge, is at the south edge of town, just to the left of Highway 132. This is the longest covered bridge across the Matapédia River, with two spans and a length of 258 feet. We notice a change of style from New Brunswick bridges, which were unpainted with vertical siding and supported by the Howe Truss. The Routhierville Bridge has horizontal siding, is painted gray with white trim, and has a Town Lattice Truss support. The New Brunswick vertical siding accentuates the height of those bridges, while the Québec horizontal siding accentuates the length of the bridges.

Elizabeth and I saw Routhierville Bridge in 1986. The bridge was damaged in 1994 when packed ice formed on the river and rose to the bridge floor. It had to be closed to repair damaged joists, but has since been reopened.

84 Longest on the Matane

François Gagnon Bridge (61-42-06) built in 1942 across the Matane River at Saint-René-de-Matane, Québec. Town Lattice Truss with two spans and a length of 170 feet.

We leave Highway 132 at Amqui and take Quebec Provincial Highway 195, heading for Matane through an area with a small concentration of covered bridges.

The first is François Gagnon Bridge at Saint-René-de-Matane. This is a long bridge, the

82. Tom Graham Bridge, New Brunswick, 1986

83. Routhierville Bridge, Québec, 1986

longest on the Matane River, with two spans and a total length of 170 feet. François Gagnon Bridge is similar in appearance to the Routhierville Bridge. We find a vantage point to see the entire bridge, with its gray horizontal siding and two long narrow openings. The bridge has had recent repairs including the addition of steel girders.

85 *Jean and Gerald*

Jean Chassé Bridge (61-42-01), near St. René, Québec, built in 1945. A Town Lattice Truss with 145-foot span crosses the Matane River.

Jean Chassé Bridge is two and one-half miles north of St. René on Highway 195, then one-quarter mile left on Range VII Road. Elizabeth and I met Gerald Arbour and his wife Claude there in 1986. They were taking bridge measurements. After introducing ourselves, we learned that Gerald is president of the covered bridge society in Québec. Jean Chassé Bridge was in a sad state of neglect and they were gathering information to prepare for a campaign to have the bridge improved.

As a result of that chance meeting, we became the members of Société Québecoise des Ponts Couverts, Inc., and later in the year began receiving copies of the newsletter *Le Pontage*. Fortunately for us, it comes with an English translation. The Arbours were planning a covered bridge tour of the west, and later I sent them information about the covered bridges in Washington State.

Interlude on the St. Lawrence

We stayed overnight at Matane in 1986 and enjoyed our stay. It was a short walk from the motel to a restaurant that overlooked the St. Lawrence River. The river here is far too wide to see across. Further southwest, near Bic, we stopped

84. François Gagnon Bridge, Québec, 1986

85. Jean Chassé Bridge, Québec, 1986

at the beach. The tide was out and we saw extensive tidal flats. We could hear voices and eventually were able to make out the people who were far out on the flats. This is definitely a wide river, and we were unable to see across it here either.

Camping near large cities worked well for us, as we arrived in the evening, spent most of the next day sightseeing in the city, and continued bridge hunting the following day. One camp-out was on the St. Lawrence River across from Québec City. The following day, we took a self-guided walking tour of the city and enjoyed a scenic boat ride on the St. Lawrence River.

86

The Light at the End of the Tunnel

Perreault Bridge (61-06-01), at Notre-Dame-des-Pins, Québec, built in 1928. Four spans and a 495-foot Town Lattice Truss across the Chaudière River.

The next bridge on our tour is to the south of Québec City on Quebec Provincial Highway 173 to Notre-Dame-des-Pins. The Perreault Bridge is four and one-half miles past the junction with Highway 108, then right one-half mile. The bridge, which is not open to traffic, is 495 feet long with four spans. It is longer than the Cornish-Windsor Bridge across the Connecticut River between New Hampshire and Vermont.

We saw Perreault Bridge on a bright July day in 1986. The long bridge, the huge concrete piers, the sunlight, and the sparkling waters of Chaudière River provided a cheerful scene. Our photos, however, were disappointing, as the bridge was dark against its bright surroundings. Inside, the Perreault Bridge is a long tunnel with a bright light at the end. The bridge was painted dark green when we saw it, but has since been painted red.

86. Perreault Bridge, Québec, 1986. At right is the interior showing the Town Lattice Truss.

Street scene, Québec City, 1986

87

The Old One is Photographed

Fisher Hill/McVetty-McKerry Bridge (61-18-08), near Gould, Québec, built in 1893, a Town Lattice Truss with two spans and a length of 206 feet. Crosses the Rivière au Saumon.

Heading southwest from Beauceville on Highway 108 to Gould, we go north on the road to Weedon Center for two and one-half miles. The road crosses Rivière au Saumon on a concrete bridge and Fisher Hill/McVetty-McKerry Bridge is just to the right.

87. Fisher Hill/McVetty–McKerry Bridge, Québec, 1986

Fisher Hill Bridge was an almost instant favorite with us. The bridge is in an open setting across the river, and is colorful with a red roof and impressive with a stone pier and abutments, and wide, continuous openings along the sides. We shared the bridge and its surroundings with several boys. It was their playground that day, but they gave us permission to be there and to walk on the bridge.

115

88. Milby Bridge, Québec, 1986

An Ordinary Kind of Bridge

Milby Bridge (61-67-03), near Huntingville, Québec, crosses Moe River with a 79-foot Town Lattice Truss span. Built in 1872.

We continue west on Provincial Highway 108 and stay overnight at Sherbrooke. Several ordinary covered bridges are nearby and we include one in this tour. To find Milby Bridge, we find the place where Highway 147 joins 108 (we had trouble with this one), go south on 147 for three miles, then just left. Milby Bridge is small and unassuming, with a single span across the Moe River. The bridge has faded red, vertical siding.

Montreal, Grand Remous, Ottawa

Savoyard Bridge (61-25-15), a 239-foot crossing of the Gatineau River, near Grand Remous, Québec. Built in 1931 as a Town Lattice Truss with two spans.

We approached Montreal on a drizzly day on 1986, found a motel on the St. Lawrence River across from the city, and then drove to a restaurant. The young waiter did not speak English, but he brought us a satisfying meal. We got hopelessly lost trying to get back to the motel. I went into a fast food restaurant expecting a language barrier and said "We're lost." The manager replied (in English) "You're not lost. You're here." He was right. A sympathetic bystander gave us his map and directions, and soon we were safely "home." The rain abated at sunset and we were treated to

89. Savoyard Bridge, Québec, 1986

a view of the Montreal skyline with a deep orange sky as a backdrop. The next day, we took a bus tour of Montreal highlighted by a tour through Notre Dame Cathedral.

Our route is northwest out of Montreal on Quebec Provincial highways 15 and 117 to Grand Remous, then south on Provincial Highway 105 for two and one-half miles and east one-tenth of a mile to Savoyard Bridge. The long, red bridge stretches across the Gatineau River, and seen from the highway, is an unexpected and spectacular scene with the river cascading down below the bridge and with logs from an earlier log drive caught in the backwaters of the river.

We continue south on Provincial Highway 105 to Ottawa, Canada's capital city. The weather cooperates and we are able to camp two nights near Ottawa. We have a full day to explore the city on foot, by double-decker bus, and by boat on the Rideau Canal.

 Interlude at West Montrose

Kissing Bridge (59-51-01), at West Montrose, Ontario, built in 1881 with a two span Queenpost Truss, 190 feet in length across Grand River.

The only covered bridge remaining in Ontario is located in West Montrose. The town is west of Toronto and north of Kitchener. When we arrived in West Montrose, we were also at Kissing Bridge which crosses the Grand River near the town center. Betty's sister, Joyce, and Joyce's husband Don were with us in 1992. We arrived in time for lunch, so we enjoyed our lunch in a picnic area next to the bridge.

Satisfied inside, we could now appreciate Kissing Bridge with its deep red vertical siding, sculptured portals, and considerable length. Inside, the lower half of the Queenpost Truss is covered by white boards, but the upper half can

117

Interlude at West Montrose, Ontario

90. Kissing Bridge, Ontario, 1992

118

91. Gudgeonville Bridge, Pennsylvania, 1992

A View with a Bridge

Gudgeonville Bridge (38-25-03), near Girard, Pennsylvania, built about 1868 with a single 83-foot Multiple Kingpost Truss span of Elk Creek.

be seen. The two spans, each 95 feet in length, are unusually long for this type of support. Outside, long steel beams extend under the deck, and diagonal iron rods have been added to help support the bridge.

Our visit was highlighted when our fuel pump expired in the middle of Kissing Bridge. The car, with gasps and jerks, used the fuel remaining in the fuel line to get us to the middle of the main intersection of West Montrose. We found a bench where we could sit until the wrecker arrived and towed us to Elmira. Mechanics at a garage installed a new fuel pump and had us on our way. We reached Niagara Falls later than intended, so we deferred visiting the falls until the next morning, August 18, 1992.

We viewed Niagara Falls—always the same, but always new. A mist was coming from above as well as from below. We thought, if it's raining we must be approaching covered bridge country.

Our route goes west along the south shore of Lake Erie. Exiting from Interstate 90 to Girard, Pennsylvania, on U.S. 20, we go south one and three-quarter miles on Tannery Road, which is one-quarter mile east of the junction of U.S. 20 and Pennsylvania 18, right three-quarters of a mile on Beckman Road, and three-quarters of a mile on Gudgeonville Road. With luck, we have

92. State Road Bridge, Ohio, 1992

gone down a hill to the Gudgeonville Bridge. It crosses Elk Creek just below a high sandstone hill.

The scenery around the bridge is impressive. I liked the view from the creek of the bridge, with its weathered siding and the steep, sandy hillside behind it. The 83-foot Multiple Kingpost Truss span is sturdily built with wide timbers and the deck has a "positive camber," or slight upward slope, to the center of the bridge.

A New Bridge

State Road Bridge (35-04-58), near Kelloggs-ville, Ohio. Built in 1983 with two spans and a 157-foot Town Lattice Truss across Conneaut Creek.

Ashtabula County in the northeast corner of Ohio, has a covered bridge festival each year. The county has about a dozen old covered bridges and several new ones. We see one of the newer ones first. We exit Interstate 90 south on Ohio State Highway 7 to Ohio 84, then go west two and one-quarter miles to State Road, and right one and one-half miles to the bridge.

New covered bridges are old hat to Ashtabula County. The county engineer, using funds from the Comprehensive Employment and Training Agency (CETA) along with CETA trainees, built State Road Bridge. It is an authentic Town Lattice Truss structure with two spans and a length of 157 feet across Conneaut Creek. The materials and construction techniques are new, but the structure is as authentic as any older covered bridge.

93   *A Bridge with a Past*

Mechanicsville Bridge (35-04-18), near Austinburg, Ohio. Built in 1867 as a single span 154-foot Howe Truss and Arch span of Grand River.

Returning to Interstate 90, west to Ohio 45 south to Ohio 307, then west two and one-half miles and left three-quarters of a mile on Mechanicsville Road, we find the old Mechanicsville Bridge.

This bridge, aging and now bypassed, shows a lot of character. The vertical siding is dark gray, interspersed with lighter gray boards. There are small rectangular openings in the sides, and an open strip below the eaves extends the full length of the bridge. Built as a single span resting on cut stone abutments, it was later strengthened by adding steel columns near the center to help counteract the effects of old age. The Howe Truss has help from arches built of fifteen layers of two-by-eight inch timbers.

94   *Changing with the Times*

Harpersfield Bridge (35-04-19), built in 1868 as a two span Howe Truss 234 feet long, crosses the Grand River at the south edge of Harpersfield, Ohio, on old Route 534.

Return to Ohio 307 and continue west to one-quarter mile west of Ohio 534, then south one-quarter mile on old Route 534.

A bridge in a busy spot must either shape up or give up. Harpersfield Bridge, built across the Grand River in 1868, has kept up with the times and appears destined for a long and useful life.

93. Mechanicsville Bridge, Ohio, 1992

94. Harpersfield Bridge, Ohio, 1992

The original bridge had two spans, and a third, steel span was added when a dam built downstream made the river wider at the location of the bridge.

Harpersfield Bridge had a covered pedestrian walkway added on one side and traffic lights have been installed to give the two-way auto traffic alternate chances to cross on the single lane. The bridge, with its recent renovations, looked good in 1992. We could view the bridge from both sides, head-on, and we took a quick look at the inside to see the Howe Truss.

Greenfield Village at Dearborn

Ackley Bridge (22-82-01), a 75-foot long Multiple Kingpost span of a pond at Greenfield Village near Dearborn, Michigan, built in 1832.

Our tour continues west along the south shore of Lake Erie, past Cleveland and Toledo, and into Michigan. North and east, at Greenfield Village

in Dearborn, Michigan, is another covered bridge. We have not included Ackley Bridge on this tour, but the bridge is well worth seeing, as are the many attractions which Henry Ford gathered at Greenfield Village. This old bridge, dated 1832, was purchased by Henry Ford and moved here from Pennsylvania in 1937. It has horizontal wood siding and a shake roof.

White Bridge by Brown

White Bridge (22-34-01), near Smyrna, Michigan. Built in 1869 with a 116-foot Brown Truss span of the Flat River.

Our route goes north and west to Lansing, west on Interstate 96 to Michigan State Highway 66, north to Michigan 44, west to Michigan 91, south at Cooks Corners to Smyrna, and southwest on Covered Bridge Road to White Bridge.

White Bridge carries the road across the Flat River on a 116-foot Brown Truss span. The bridge and its surroundings have a rustic charac-

95. White Bridge, Michigan, 1989

ter and look as if they have always been here together. The vertical wood siding is several shades of weathered brown with a few white boards mixed in.

The Brown Truss is unique to Michigan. It has crossed diagonal wood beams with vertical wood beams only at the ends and at the center. All of the original timbers were floated on the Flat River from the sawmill to the bridge site.

Bonus Bridge in a Park

Fallasburg Bridge (22-41-02), a 100-foot Brown Truss span of Flat River built in 1871. Near Lowell, Michigan.

Fallasburg Bridge is another Brown Truss covered bridge and is nearby in a county park north of Lowell. Fallasburg Bridge is well worth seeing and has convenient access. It is four miles north

of Lowell on Lincoln Avenue and right three-quarters of a mile. The bridge has dark siding, a rusted tin roof, and an open setting in the park.

Better to Raise a Bridge Than to Raze It

Langley Bridge (22-75-01), near Centreville, Michigan. Three spans and a 282-foot Howe Truss across the St. Joseph River (Sturgis Lake). Built in 1887.

Our tour route takes us south of Grand Rapids, through Kalamazoo on U.S. 131, east on Michigan 86 to Centreville, and three miles north on Covered Bridge Road.

Langley Bridge, built in 1887 across the St. Joseph River, was threatened when the river was dammed in 1910 creating Sturgis Lake. The bridge had to be raised or demolished. It was

123

raised eight feet and placed on steel beams. We visited it in 1986 with Betty's sister, Joyce, and brother-in-law, Don. The red vertical siding and white trim at the portals and around the long horizontal openings are most impressive.

97 Amish Country

Coburn/Spencerville Bridge (14-17-01) at Spencerville, Indiana. Built in 1873 with a 160-foot Smith Truss span of St. Joseph River.

We head south on Michigan State Highway 66 into Indiana, east on Interstate 80 and south on Interstate 69 to a car museum at Auburn and a covered bridge at Spencerville. The Auburn Museum displays Auburns, Cords, and Duesen-bergs, once built there, plus additional makes of cars and other attractions—a most fascinating place. I grew up wishing I could own a Cord, a wish beyond reach. Now, at least, I could look.

Coburn/Spencerville Bridge is southeast of Auburn at Spencerville and just right of Michigan State Highway 1 on Front Street. We first saw Coburn Bridge in 1977, with Betty's sister, Shirley, and Shirley's husband Al. Now, eighteen years later in 1995, we were back. The bridge had been renovated and looked newer, but it had not really changed. We watched Amish horse-drawn buggies and wagons cross the bridge. Coburn Bridge has white portals, red vertical siding, and openings on the sides covered by a narrow roof.

The Smith Truss supporting the bridge is similar to the Long Truss, with crossed diagonal wood beams but with vertical wood beams only at the ends of the truss.

96. Langley Bridge, Michigan, 1986

97. Coburn/Spencerville Bridge, Indiana, 1995

Cord auto at Auburn Museum, Auburn, Indiana

98   *Rising from the Ashes*

Roann Bridge (14-85-01) at north edge of Roann, Indiana, on Old Chippewa Road. Built in 1872 with two spans and a 300-foot Howe Truss crossing of Eel River.

In 1992, Elizabeth and I took a break at Fort Wayne, Indiana. She looked through genealogical records at the Allen Library in Fort Wayne searching for information about her Cornish ancestors who had migrated to the United States about 1870.

Back to our search for covered bridges, we left Fort Wayne and went west on U.S. 24 and north on Indiana State Highway 15 to Roann. We were looking for Roann Bridge. Our covered bridge quarterlies had been telling about the loss to arson in 1991 of one span of the bridge and the efforts to raise money to rebuild it. We arrived there in August of 1992 expecting to see ruins, but instead we saw Roann Bridge rebuilt and looking new. A painter on a scaffolding was applying red paint to the new siding.

The people who cared about Roann Bridge and contributed to rebuild it decided to protect their investment. An automatic sprinkler system was installed and is designed to extinguish any fire within seconds.

99   *Photograph My Good Side*

Cedarburg Bridge (49-46-01), at the north edge of Cedarburg, Wisconsin. Built in 1876 as a single 120-foot Town Lattice Truss span of Cedar Creek.

98. Roann Bridge, Indiana, 1992

99. Cedarburg Bridge, Wisconsin, 1989. Below, wooden pegs in the bridge's Town Lattice Truss.

Our tour heads north on Indiana State Highway 15 and west on U.S. 30 into Illinois, around the south end of Lake Michigan into Wisconsin. We drive north of Milwaukee on Interstate 43 to Wisconsin 60 and exit west to Cedarburg. We go north for one and one-quarter miles from the junction of Wisconsin 60 and Wisconsin 143 to Covered Bridge Road.

Cedarburg Bridge was built in 1876 with a 120-foot span of Cedar Creek. The bridge has an attractive location at a park with the grass and trees providing an appropriate setting for the grand old bridge. This is the good side of the bridge. On the other side, a new bridge crowds the old one and detracts from the appearance of the old bridge.

We photographed Cedarburg Bridge from its good side, including the landscaped foreground with the newer bridge barely noticeable in the background. Inside, we can see the wooden pegs at each crossing of the diagonal beams, which bind them together into the strong Town Lattice Truss.

127

B20. Chequamegon/Smith Rapids Bridge, Wisconsin, 1992

 A New Bridge for Wisconsin

Chequamegon/Smith Rapids Bridge (49-51-01), on Forest Road 148 west of Minocqua, Wisconsin. Built in 1991 with a 90-foot Town Lattice Truss span of the South Fork of the Flambeau River.

We had learned that a new covered bridge had been built in northern Wisconsin and we looked for it in 1992 on our way back to Spokane. We drove about twenty-seven miles west of Minacqua, Wisconsin, on Wisconsin 70 to Forest Road 148. The bridge provides a crossing of the South Fork of the Flambeau River. This is recreation and sportsman country with a forest campsite adjacent to the bridge.

Smith Rapids Bridge is an authentic covered bridge built in 1991 with modern materials including laminated wood trusses and modern construction techniques. A plaque on the bridge indicates it received an award in 1992 as outstanding engineering project in Wisconsin.

 A Romantic Shelter

Red Mill Bridge (49-69-A) near Waupaca, Wisconsin. A 40-foot long covered pedestrian bridge crossing the Crystal River with a Town Lattice Truss.

Near Waupaca, Wisconsin, a mill was built in 1885 known as the Red Mill. It is a popular tourist destination with a water wheel, a small chapel, and a covered pedestrian crossing of the Crystal River. It is a romantic setting where couples may be married at the chapel and pose beside the bridge for a prized photographic memento of their special day.

Red Mill Bridge, Wisconsin, 1989, a romantic shelter

Red Mill Bridge is identified by the National Society for the Preservation of Covered Bridges as a "romantic shelter." It is listed in their booklet Romantic Shelters and is not in their World Guide to Covered Bridges, which is a listing of authentic covered wooden bridges for vehicles. Our book is about covered bridges. We include this romantic shelter to explain the difference, and because we like our photo of Red Mill Bridge taken in 1989.

How to Park a Bridge

Zumbrota Bridge (23-25-01), at Zumbrota, Minnesota, built in 1869 with a 120-foot Town Lattice Truss across the Zumbro River.

The next, and last, covered bridge on our tour is at Zumbrota, Minnesota. The fastest way there from Cedarburg, Wisconsin is west on Wisconsin State Highway 60 to Interstate 90, west on I-90 to Rochester, Minnesota, then north on U.S. 52 to Zumbrota.

Zumbrota Bridge carried local and state highway traffic including stagecoaches across the Zumbro River in town for sixty-three years. The bridge was retired in 1932 and moved to the city park in 1970. This is where Betty and I saw Zumbrota Bridge in 1989.

Zumbrota Bridge has been returned to the river. It was announced in March of 1997 that the bridge would be reinforced with steel bolts and steel beams, rolled back to and placed across the Zumbro River. The bridge has been returned to where it belongs, across the river, and only a

100. Zumbrota Bridge, Minnesota, 2002

block from where it originally stood. With daughters Mary and Susan in 2002, I saw the bridge spanning the Zumbro River.

We have traveled about three thousand miles from Woodstock, New Brunswick, to Zumbrota, Minnesota, a long drive in eastern Canada and past the Great Lakes in the United States.

Modified Town Lattice Truss, Zumbrota Bridge

Chapter Seven

GHOST TO GHOST AND
BACK TO THE PRESENT

A Ghostly Tour

Our tour route returns south to Rochester, Minnesota, and goes west on Interstate 90 to Spokane, Washington, a distance of fifteen hundred miles. This is a good time to remember and recognize a few of the covered bridges that once existed in a Canadian province and in several states where covered bridges no longer exist. Here are some ghostly reminders in our ghost-to-ghost tour of the past.

Nova Scotia once had eight covered bridges, but they began disappearing by 1887 and the last one, Upper Kennetcook Bridge, was gone by 1967. We had crossed from Prince Edward Island to Truro, Nova Scotia, in 1986 and were not far from Upper Kennetcook. If the bridge had still been there, we would have seen it. It was low and wide, with weathered vertical siding.

Ghosting south, we pass through the District of Columbia, and we are reminded that covered bridges also existed there. The Long Bridge, nearly a mile long, was wooden and roofed. Partly burned by the British in 1814, it was restored as a partially covered, but mostly open, causeway bridge.

A covered bridge with two spans once crossed the Suwanee River in northern Florida, but it was gone before 1900. We have a stereoscope photo of it from the Florida State Archives.

At least eighteen covered bridges were built in Mississippi, and all were gone by 1953. Then, in 1966, a new bridge was added in a county park in Brookhaven. We missed our chance to see the May Bridge before it was removed in 1991.

When Arkansas planned to celebrate its centennial in 1936, Two Bayou Bridge near Camden, built in 1860, was the only remaining covered bridge in the state. The Camden Lions Club and the youth of Camden repaired the bridge and it was proudly displayed during the centennial year. In 1940, it was torn down.

The most remembered of several covered bridges that existed in Texas is the San Marcos River Bridge near Gonzales. Tall and narrow, it stood high above the river on massive stone piers, with long approach ramps to the 100-foot span. It was replaced in 1902, sat for years next to the new bridge, and finally disappeared.

Several covered bridges were built in Kansas, with a cluster around Fort Leavenworth, all well-built, set on stone piers. One, near Springdale, crossed Big Stranger Creek with a 130-foot Howe Truss. It had vertical wood siding, a wood roof, and portal openings curved at the top. The Kansas State Highway Commission renovated the bridge in 1945. With any luck, it would have been standing today, but in 1958, the bridge was struck by lightning and burned.

The Chicago, Burlington and Quincy Railroad built three covered bridges across the Big Blue River near Seward and Milford in Nebraska between 1879 and 1908. They are long gone and long forgotten.

I have seen a reference to a covered bridge at Valmont, near Boulder, Colorado. The Denver Public Library located two references in the Rocky Mountain News for me, which may or may not prove that Colorado once had a covered bridge. The first was: 23 Feb. 1866. "Valmont Items—The people are all called upon to assemble on Saturday and help raise the cover of the new bridge." And the second was: 8 June 1867. "The bridge across the creek at Valmont is now completed so that teams can cross with safety." With regard to covered bridges, this is about as ghostly as we can get.

Arizona, with low annual rainfall, is not covered bridge country, but unusual circumstances caused one to be built. White River Bridge, on old Highway 60 between San Carlos and Fort Apache, was built on the Fort Apache Indian Reservation in 1890 by the Bureau of Indian Affairs. It was uncovered and about seventy to eighty feet long. Army mules stubbornly refused to cross the bridge until siding extending from the deck to above mule eye-level was added. The bridge was also roofed. White River Bridge was wiped out by a flood in 1916, replaced, and finally removed in 1934.

The Central Pacific Railroad built some covered bridges as it extended rails east to meet the rails of the Union Pacific at Promontory Point, Utah. The bridge at Wadsworth, Nevada, was the last to be covered on that route. It crossed the Truckee River and was a tall, narrow structure with rounded portals, a gable roof, and vertical wood siding.

Three covered bridges were built in Idaho south of St. Maries on a branch railroad line. The bridges, built about 1910, crossed the St. Maries River at Lotus, Rover, and Clarkia. The Lotus and Rover bridges were 150 feet long and the Clarkia was 90 feet in length.

When Lewis and Clark reached the headwaters of the Missouri River in 1804, they named the three rivers at the Missouri's source the Jefferson, Madison, and Gallatin rivers. Nearly one hundred years later, a covered bridge crossed the Madison River at Three Forks, Montana. It was a 150-foot span, built by the Milwaukee Railroad about 1900. The trusses were covered, but the bridge was not roofed. Three Forks is on Interstate 90, on our route back to Spokane. If the bridge was still there, we could stop to see it, but it was gone by 1953.

Alaska is the last stop on our ghostly visit to the past. The U.S. Bureau of Public Roads built covered bridges in Alaska. The Texas Creek Bridge, north of Hyder, Alaska, was built in 1928. The setting was spectacular where it crossed the North Fork of Texas Creek with Texas Glacier in the background. Texas Creek Bridge became inaccessible in 1970 when a steel bridge on the road to Texas Creek was washed out. Alone and unused, the covered bridge collapsed during the winter of 1978–79.

Back to the Present

Back to the present, we have finished our tour of one hundred covered bridges, arriving back in Spokane, Washington.

It is good to be home. Elizabeth and I like Spokane. It has been our home most of the time since 1951, and the start and finish of eight major trips—plus a few minor trips—devoted to seeing covered bridges. They are represented here as one long trip with a total distance of about thirteen thousand miles, or more if you include bonus bridges.

Spokane hosted a World's Fair in 1974—Expo '74—which had an environmental theme. The Expo site was along the Spokane River and adjacent to downtown. The fair was a success. Elizabeth and I bought season passes and went many times. Friends and relatives, who came to see the fair, stayed with us. It was a bountiful year.

The fair is over, and today, in its place in the

Riverfront Park, Spokane, Washington, 1983

middle of the city on the Spokane River, we have Riverfront Park. We were there for a concert in the park in July of 1983, a competition of Scottish bagpiper's bands—a colorful show with the members of the bands dressed to the "kilt." It was a privilege to enjoy the show in this beautiful park on a sunny afternoon. A few days later, we were off on another trip.

You might ask, "If Spokane is so great, why were you always leaving?" Our answer would be, "Because we have Spokane to come home to."

Wherever you live, it is most likely not far from the meandering route we have chosen for this covered bridge tour. You can readily join the route near your home and include a covered bridge on your next trip.

Elizabeth and I saw and photographed our first covered bridge (Goodpasture Bridge in Oregon) in 1965 and our last one (Green Sergeants Bridge in New Jersey) in 1997. Together we saw over two hundred covered

bridges in twenty-nine states and four Canadian provinces.

Good-bye

In September of 2000, the walls of the house were closing in on me. It had been three years since Elizabeth and I saw our last covered bridge together. Betty died of cancer in 1999, and I was adjusting to life without her. Still, there were times....

I was ready to get away for a couple of days, so I drove north into Canada. It is beautiful country. I crossed North Arrow Lake on the car ferry and stayed overnight at Revelstoke. The next morning, my subconscious mind told me that I really wanted to see again the covered bridge in British Columbia that Elizabeth and I visited in 1989, so I headed south and west to Keremeos. As I

133

approached the Ashnola River Road Bridge, I noticed some siding was missing, so I stopped and walked to the river to get a picture.

"It's a nice day."

"It sure is."

The bridge was talking to me and I answered. Well, why not. We had met before and we were on friendly terms. Then I saw someone sitting in one of the holes in the siding. It was a young lady on her lunch break. We visited for awhile, then she bicycled back to town and her work, and the bridge was again silent. It was time for me to return to Spokane.

The house welcomed me back. It was in a much better mood than when I left. My trip was a welcome break. I visited an old friend, the Ashnola River Road Bridge, and remembered when Betty and I visited it in 1989.

Thanks, Betty, for your help and for the memories. This book is for you.

134

EPILOGUE

The Bridge Knows the Way was essentially complete in 1997, except for a few missing pieces. Our children pitched in and helped finish the task, and our story became a family affair.

My daughters, Mary and Susan, and I were finding missing pieces in 2001. Susan had traveled before with her mother and me and had already caught covered bridge fever. Mary soon became an enthusiast and the two were leading me to see more covered bridges than I had ever bargained for. We found Wertz/Red Bridge near Reading, Pennsylvania, which Betty and I were not able to see together. We saw, at North Bennington, Vermont, not only Henry Bridge, but

Bridge at the Green/Arlington Green, Vermont, 2001

Mary and Susan on whale watcher ship, Cape Cod, 2001

also Papermill Village Bridge and Silk/Locust Grove/Robinson Bridge. Mary and Susan wanted to know if there were any other covered bridges nearby, so we included the other two in Bennington County—Chiselville/High/Roaring Branch Bridge at East Arlington and Bridge at the Green/Arlington Green in West Arlington.

Bridge at the Green/Arlington Green (45-02-01) West Arlington, Vermont. 80 foot Town Lattice Truss span of Batten Kill built in 1852

We traveled to the Woodstock area of Vermont to see and photograph again Lincoln Bridge and Taftsville Bridge, which Betty and I had seen in 1986. "Are there other covered bridges around?" Yes. Middle/Union Street Bridge is in Woodstock and we walked from the motel to see it.

Mary had not seen Cornish-Windsor Bridge. It was our final covered bridge in 2001. We had plenty of time to include other attractions, including an Amish village at Lancaster, Pennsylvania; Bushkill Falls at the Delaware River Gap in New York State; a cheese and maple syrup farm out of Taftsville; Barnstable and Hyannis on Cape Cod in Massachusetts; and whale-watching and harbor boat trips.

We found time in 2002 to see and photograph Zumbrota Bridge back across the Zumbro River in Zumbrota, Minnesota. My daughters discovered there were two covered bridges in Wisconsin that their mother and I saw in 1989 and 1992, so we visited them together in 2002.

Milton could not join his sisters and me on this trip. He has photographed and kept us informed about covered bridges in Oregon and Washington. Milton and I found the new Lynch/Grist Mill/Cedar Creek Bridge in Washington and the relocated Upper Drift Creek Bridge in Oregon.

I am pleased and proud that my entire family is represented in and have contributed to *The Bridge Knows the Way.*

ACKNOWLEDGMENTS AND SOURCES

We thank the National Society for the Preservation of Covered Bridges and Society President David Wright for permission to refer to the World Guide to Covered Bridges, Covered Bridge Topics, and the Newsletter in this book.

Published by the National Society for the Preservation of Covered Bridges, the World Guide to Covered Bridges provides basic information such as name, bridge number, location, length, type of truss, and year built, for all known covered bridges worldwide. Available for $8 payable to NSPCB. Send to June Roy, 73 Ash Street, Manchester NH 03104. The Guide is scheduled to be updated in 2004.

Covered Bridge Societies

National Society for the Preservation of Covered Bridges, David Wright, President. Annual membership for individuals is $15 to the NSPCB sent to Pauline Prideaux, 143 Freeman Street Ext., Haverhill, MA 01830-4659. Membership includes Covered Bridge Topics and Newsletter published quarterly. These publications have been a primary source of information about covered bridges, including recent losses or improvements and new bridges.

Indiana Covered Bridge Society. Lynette L. Kross, President. Annual membership including quarterly Newsletter is $10 for individual or family. Send dues to John Sechrist, Treasurer, 6770 South East St., Apt. 3, Indianapolis, IN 46227-2252.

Zumbrota Covered Bridge Society (Minnesota). Annual membership is $6. Send dues to Evelyn Kiester, Treasurer, P.O. Box 15, Frontenac, MN 55026.

Covered Bridges in New Brunswick Preservation Association, Inc. Robert Alston, President. Annual membership for individuals (includes newsletter) is $10 (Canadian). Send dues to Tammy Gordon, Secretary, 527 Beaverbrook Court, Box 116, Fredericton NB E3B 1X6

New York State Covered Bridge Society, Inc. Richard Wilson, President. Annual individual membership is $10. Includes Newsletter published quarterly and Empire State Courier published three times per year. Send dues to Henry Messing, Treasurer, 958 Grove St., Elmira, NY 14901

Ohio Historic Bridge Association, David A. Simmons, President. Annual individual membership is $10. Includes Bridges and Byways published quarterly. Send dues to Joseph Wm. Charles Jr., Treasurer, 726 Newark-Granville Road, Granville, OH 43023-1451

The Covered Bridge Society of Oregon, Jerry Russell, President. Annual membership is $15. Includes The Bridge Tender published quarterly. Send dues to Jeannine Schmeltzer, 24595 SW Neill Rd., Sherwood OR 97140.

The Theodore Burr Covered Bridge Society of Pennsylvania. Thomas E. Walczak, President. Annual individual membership is $10 paid to Society. Includes Pennsylvania Crossings published three times per year and Wooden Spans published twice per year. Send dues to Carolyn L. Warner, Treasurer, 905 Impounding Dam Road, Hanover, PA 17331-9666.

Société Québecoise des Ponts Couverts, Inc. Gerald Arbour, President. Publishes Le Pontage quarterly newsletter. Gerald Arbour, 2126 Delorimier, Longueuil PQ, Canada, J4K 3N9. The society is not currently in existence.

References

Adams, Kramer A. 1963. Covered Bridges of the West, a History and a Guide: Washington, Oregon, California. Berkeley, CA: Howell-North.

Allen, Richard Sanders. 1974. Covered Bridges of the Northeast. Brattleboro, VT: Stephen Greene Press.

————. 1970a. Covered Bridges of Middle West. Brattleboro, VT: Stephen Greene Press.

————. 1970b. Covered Bridges of the South. Brattleboro, VT: Stephen Greene Press.

————. 1959. Covered Bridges of the Middle Atlantic States. Brattleboro, VT: Stephen Greene Press.

————. Covered Bridge Topics. Published by the National Society for the Preservation of Covered Bridges. (selected articles)

Auvil, Myrtle. 1977. Covered Bridges of West Virginia, Past and Present. Parsons, WV: McClain Printing Co.

Baker, T. Lindsay. 1986. Building the Lone Star. College Station, TX: Texas A&M University Press

Barna, Ed. 1996. Covered Bridges of Vermont. Woodstock, VT: The Countryman Press.

Berfield, Rick L. 2003. Covered Bridges of New York State: A Guide. Syracuse, NY: Syracuse University Press.

Brydon, Norman F. 1970. Of Time, Fire and the River: The Story of New Jersey's Covered Bridges. New Brunswick, NJ: Rutgers University Press.

Caravan, Jill. 1995. American Covered Bridge: A Pictorial History. Philadelphia, PA: Courage Books.

Cockrell, Nick and Bill. 1978. Roofs Over Rivers: A Guide to Oregon's Covered Bridges. Beaverton, OR: Touchstone Press.

Coldrick, Helen. 1992. New Brunswick's Covered Bridges. St. John, New Brunswick. Neptune Publishing Co. Ltd.

Congdon, Herbert Wheaton. 1979. The Covered Bridge, An Old American Landmark Whose Romance, Stability and Craftsmanship are Typified by the Structures Remaining in Vermont. Middlebury, VT: Vermont Books.

Conwill, Joseph D. 2003. Maine's Covered Bridges. Charleston, SC: Arcadia Publishing.

Eaton, Thelma. 1968. The Covered Bridges of Illinois. Ann Arbor, MI: Edwards Brothers, Inc.

Gillis, Stephen and John. 1988. No Faster Than A Walk: The Covered Bridges of New Brunswick. Fredericton, New Brunswick, Canada: Goose Lane Editions. Ltd.

Harrington, Lyn and Richard. 1976. Covered Bridges of Central and Eastern Canada. Toronto, Canada: McGraw-Hill Ryerson.

Howard, Andrew. 1979. Covered Bridges of Massachusetts: A Guide. Unionville, CT: The Village Press.

————. 1982. Covered Bridges of Maine: A Guide. Unionville, CT: The Village Press.

————. 1985. Covered Bridges of Connecticut: A Guide. Unionville, CT: The Village Press.

Krekeler, Brenda C. 1989. Covered Bridges Today. Canton, OH: Daring Books, 1989.

Missouri Mills and Covered Bridges. 1972. Jefferson City, MO: Missouri Tourism Commission.

Morley, Sylvanus Griswold. 1938. The Covered Bridges of California. Berkeley, CA: University of California Press

Myrick, David F. 1992. Railroads of Nevada and Eastern California. Reno, NV: University of Nevada Press.

Nelson, Lee H. 1976. A Century of Oregon Covered Bridges: 1851–1952. Oregon Historical Society.

Sangster, Tom and Dess. 1980. Alabama's Covered Bridges. Bay Minette, AL: Coffeetable Publications

Smith, Elmer L. 1960. Covered Bridges of Pennsylvania Dutchland. Whitmer, PA: Applied Arts.

Smith, Lorna J. 2001. Covered Bridges of Washington State. Clatskanie, Oregon. The Owls Nest.

Swanson, Leslie C. 1970. Covered Bridges in Illinois, Iowa and Wisconsin. Moline, IL: Published by author.

Wagerman, Clara B. 1952. The Covered Bridges of New England. Rutland, Vermont. Charles E. Tuttle Co.

Wells, Rosalie. 1931. Covered Bridges in America. New York: William Edwin Rudge.

White, Warren H. 2003. Covered Bridges in the Southeastern United States. Jefferson, NC: McFarland & Co., Inc.

Wiebel, Jerry, Ed. 1998. Life in the Slow Lane. Greendale, WI: Reiman Publications

Woolfolk, Miriam L. 1987. Kentucky's Covered Bridges. Published by author.

World Guide to Covered Bridges. Revised edition, 1989. Bill Heisel, Editorial Coordinator. The National Society for the Preservation of Covered Bridges, Inc.: NSPCB World Guide Steering Committee.

Zacher, Susan M. 1982. The Covered Bridges of Pennsylvania: A Guide. Harrisburg, Commonwealth of Pensylvania: Pennsylvania Historical and Museum Commission.

Additional sources of information on the covered bridges mentioned in this book.

Historic markers and historic literature at covered bridge sites.

The covered bridges themselves as we experienced and photographed them.

Sources for information on covered bridges on "A Ghostly Tour."

Blue River Bridge in Nebraska: Covered Bridges of the Middle West.

Long Bridge in District of Columbia: Covered Bridge Topics.

May's Bridge in Mississippi: Covered Bridge Topics.

San Marcos River Bridge in Texas: Building the Lone Star.

Springdale Bridge in Kansas: Covered Bridges of the South.

St. Maries River Bridges in Idaho: Covered Bridges of the Middle West.

Suwanee River Bridge in Florida: Florida State Archives. Tallahassee, Florida.

Texas Creek Bridge in Alaska: Connecticut River Valley Covered Bridge Society Bulletin, Spring 1980.

Three Forks Bridge in Montana, W.R. McGee, Livingston, Montana.

Two Bayou Bridge: Arkansas History Commission.

Upper Kennetcook Bridge in Nova Scotia Public Archives of Nova Scotia. Halifax, Nova Scotia.

Valmont Bridge in Colorado: Denver Public Library, Denver, Colorado.

Wadsworth Bridge in Nevada: Railroads of Nevada and Eastern California.

White River Bridge in Arizona: Covered Bridges of the West.

Photo Credits

Photographs were taken by Frank or Elizabeth Tobie, except for the following, which were taken by our daughters, Mary and Susan.

Mary Fagan:
Cornish-Windsor Bridge, New Hampshire/Vermont, 2001
Papermill Village Bridge, Vermont, 2001
Taftsville Bridge, Vermont, 2001

Susan Heyen:
Bridge at the Green/Arlington Green, Vermont, 2001
Henry Bridge, Vermont, 2001
Lincoln Bridge, Vermont, 2001

INDEX